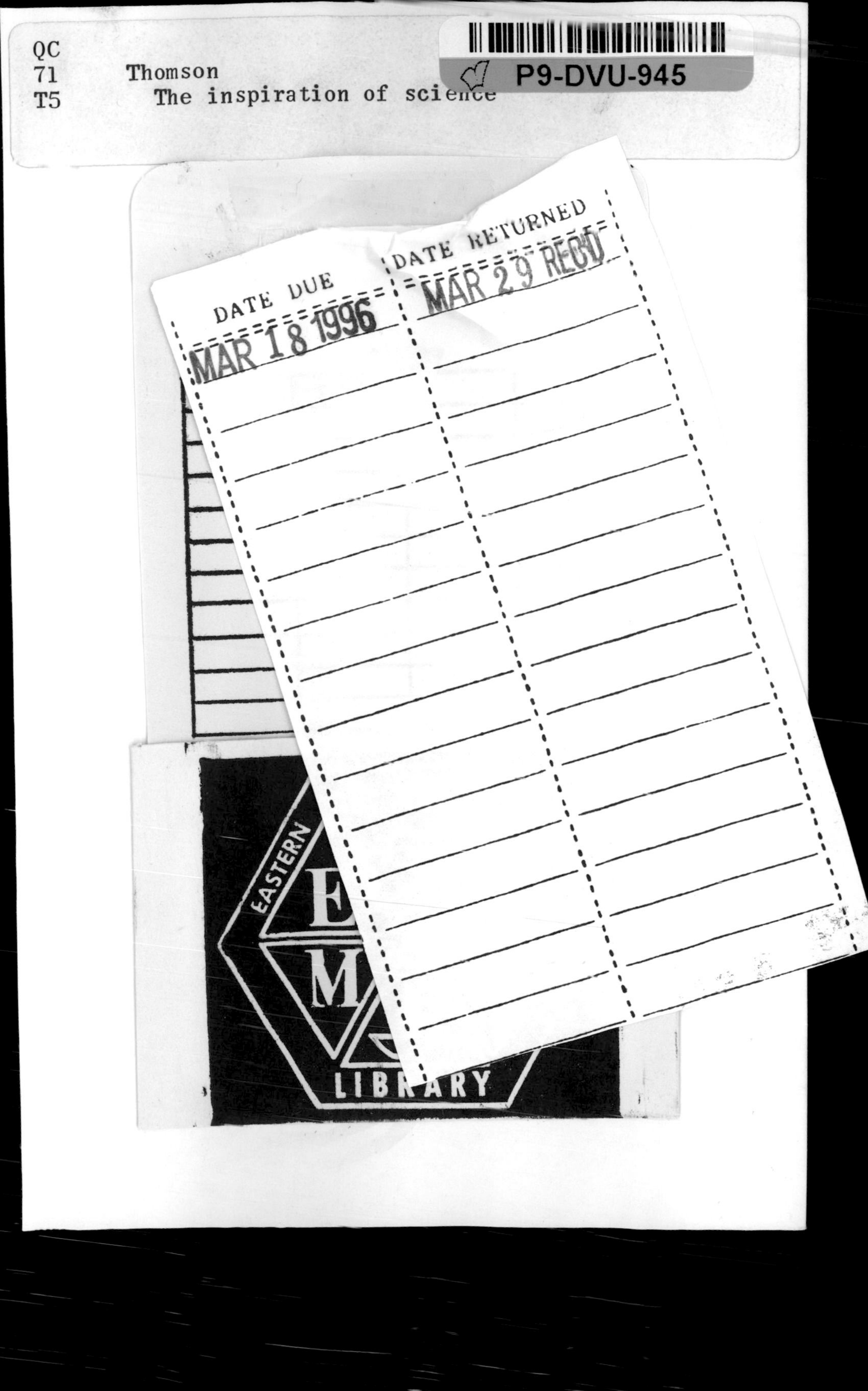
DATE DUE
DATE RETURNED
MAR 18 1996
MAR 29 REC'D
EASTERN
LIBRARY

THE INSPIRATION OF SCIENCE

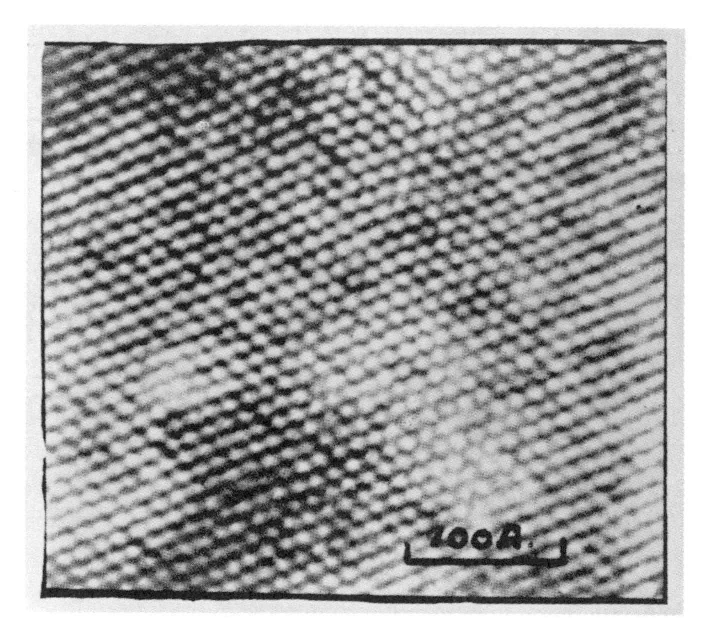

Fig. 1. Arrangement of Atoms in Gold and Copper

This is a direct photograph in an electron microscope of very thin film of these two metals superposed. The arrangement of atoms is the same in both, but the spacings are rather greater for gold than copper. In consequence the patterns are sometimes in, and sometimes out of step. This 'beat' pattern is large enough to see, though the individual patterns would not be. G. A. Bassett, J. W. Menter and D. W. Pashley (*Proc. Roy. Soc.* A.246, 345–68, 1958).

THE INSPIRATION OF SCIENCE

SIR GEORGE THOMSON

F.R.S., NOBEL LAUREATE, MASTER OF CORPUS
CHRISTI COLLEGE, CAMBRIDGE

LONDON
OXFORD UNIVERSITY PRESS
NEW YORK TORONTO

PRINTED IN THE UNITED STATES OF AMERICA

CONTENTS

ILLUSTRATIONS

PREFACE

This book is a modest attempt to explain the kind of way in which scientists think, especially when engaged in research. Admittedly it is based entirely on my own experience, reading, and observation, which are limited to physics and a very little chemistry, but I suspect, though I cannot prove, that the difference from other sciences is not as great as some exponents of them seem to think. Anyhow, no one now can speak for the whole of science and one is more likely to get a useful picture across if one does not try to fill too large a screen. The book deals almost exclusively with what is called 'pure' science, an intellectual pursuit whose rewards are quite different from those of technology. This last is equally exciting and quite as difficult, but as different as farming is from breeding roses or architecture from sculpture.

It is obviously impossible to describe scientific thought without giving examples, and this means attempting to explain a good deal of physics, including many of the most important principles. However, I have kept the facts down to the minimum, and the book is in no sense a textbook, even a popular one. I have not hesitated to repeat statements of facts where they are needed for another argument, and have tried to make each chapter independent so as to demand as little as possible from the reader's memory. I hope the book will prove readable to those with little or no physics. The very short biographical sketches are all of men whom I knew directly or through a lively family tradition. In spite of temptation, no living physicists are included. Even with these restrictions the selection does not represent my judgement of the most important figures. I have included only those whose work dealt with ideas that fitted the scheme of the book. To avoid the need for many interruptions of the argument to explain technical terms a glossary of the principal ones is given on pp. 139–146.

I would like to express my thanks to Professor W. H. McCrea, F.R.S., of the University of London. He must not be held responsible for the opinions expressed there but his comments on part of Chapter V were most helpful. I should also like to thank my secretary Mrs. Bainbridge, for her care and unfailing efforts in the preparation of the manuscript.

Cambridge
August 1961

ACKNOWLEDGEMENTS

The drawing on page 25 is reproduced by permission of Edward Arnold (Publishers) Ltd., from Crowther: *Ions, Electrons and Ionizing Radiation*; that on page 28 by permission of G. Bell & Sons Ltd., from Bragg: *Introduction to Crystal Analysis*. The photograph facing page 36 by permission of Longmans, Green & Co. Ltd., from J. J. Thomson: *Rays of Positive Electricity*. The drawing on page 81 by permission of the Cambridge University Press, from J. Cox: *Mechanics*. The photograph facing page 83 by permission of the Hutchinson Publishing Group from E. Larsen: *An American in Europe*. The cartoon on page 91 is reproduced by permission of *Punch*. The photograph facing page 99 by permission of Pergamon Press Ltd., from Rochester & Wilson: *Cloud Chamber Photographs of the Cosmic Radiation*.

THE INSPIRATION OF SCIENCE

I

INTRODUCTION: WHAT IS SCIENCE TRYING TO DO?

SCIENCE is essentially a search for truth. It has been so ever since the days of Thales, when a number of individuals, citizens of the prosperous Greek cities of western Asia Minor, began the practice of abstract thought unconnected with religion—this was the greatest of the many great achievements of the Greek race. At first there was no distinction between what would now be called philosophy, mathematics, and science. It was hoped, very reasonably, that valid conclusions about the world could be reached by sheer force of intellect. As time went on, two lines of work strengthened this hope and turned it into a belief. First came the successes of Greek geometry, including the magnificent edifice which, by the name of Euclid, the schoolboys in the western world knew in slightly varying form for just on two thousand years. Now geometry is peculiar in that it may either be an exercise in mathematical logic or a statement of facts about the outside world. The Greeks must have had at least an inkling of this, for Euclid's famous axiom on parallels is strikingly different from his other axioms—such as 'the whole is greater than the part'—in that it is by no means obvious, though on it depends most of what follows. It can be stated in many different but equivalent forms, one being that only one line can be drawn through a given point parallel to another given line. This is sufficiently reasonable that it is possible to persuade oneself that it is logically necessary, especially when one knows that it leads to consistent and important conclusions which never outrage experience.

In fact, however, this is not so. Other varieties of geometry are logically possible and the truth of Euclid's geometry for measurements on earth is merely a very accurately established experimental fact; its truth over astronomical space is open to quite genuine doubt.

The other great scientific success of the Greeks was in astronomy. Here they approached much nearer to modern science for they made observations, surprisingly accurate ones, of the stars and especially of the planets and used these to form and to check theories of the motions of the heavens.* But with things on earth they were less successful. They knew that amber when rubbed attracted chaff, that a stone from a place in Asia Minor called Magnesia attracted iron, and had observed that a pole sticking out of the water seemed bent; but they made no real progress with the corresponding sciences. It is sometimes said that this failure was due to an unwillingness to experiment. No doubt up to a point this is true, but I think that there is something more. They did in fact perform occasional experiments besides their many astronomical observations; theirs was much more a failure to realize the importance of these apparently trivial occurrences. The heavens were impressive and grand, perhaps the abode of gods or even of something greater than the gods. Little bits of chaff and shreds of iron were amusing but hardly of the first importance. This is a very natural attitude indeed.

It is the greatest discovery in method which science has made that the apparently trivial, the merely curious, may be clues to an understanding of the deepest principles of Nature. One can hardly blame the Greeks. Even with Newton behind him, Swift could be witty at the expense of the Royal Society in his account of the 'projectors' of Laputa with their studies of cucumbers as a source of sunlight—and Swift, though an unpleasant creature, was no fool. Just how the discovery came about is not clear. It is the great thing that marks off our age from others, and may well have had several independent causes. Among these, probably, was the importance of magnetism for navigation and of optics for spectacles. Gunnery perhaps added a little, and made Galileo's new mechanics sound rather less improbable. But a greater cause was the excitement that came from the discovery of the way round

* They also made considerable use of Babylonian observations.

Africa to India and then of the New World. In an age in which the wildest projects of geographical discovery had proved successful it was natural to try others of a different kind, to open the mind and ask more searching questions on matters nearer at hand. The first discovery must always be that there are things worth discovering. So the apparent trivialities of the stone from Magnesia and of amber grew in importance and since the time of Maxwell it has been clear to the discerning that the ideas behind them are as fundamental as any in the world, not even excluding that of matter.

Science is both valued and dreaded nowadays for what it may lead to in practice, but this is only one aspect of it and not the one most vividly present to the mind of the average scientist. If he is conscientious, and I think most of us are, he may satisfy uneasy feelings that he is spending most of his life doing what he enjoys by reflecting that the health and the standard of living of most of the world have been greatly improved by the discoveries of his fellows, that indeed present civilization would be impossible without them. He may also feel it his duty to point out the dangers of some discoveries and to protest against actual or prospective misuse of them. But even if he is in fact working on applied science it is likely that it is the intellectual side of the problem that really appeals to him, and in particular the way in which its threads interweave with those of seemingly quite different questions.

Apart from giving pleasure to scientists, the intellectual value of science is two-fold. It is a great achievement of the human mind in its own right and it supplies a test to which all wider theories must conform. Science and philosophy aim ultimately at the same end, to understand the world and ourselves, but they start from opposite ends. Science starts from a detailed examination of particulars and passes, if it can, from them to more general ideas. Philosophy starts from the general and tries to explain the particular. It may be said that science does not touch the really fundamental things; indeed its method is the modest one of starting with the humble, even the apparently trivial. It has gone a long way since the Greeks and there are yet no signs of it stopping. It builds a broad-based pyramid resting firmly on observed facts. Philosophy has indeed produced a number of systems of great brilliance, but there has seldom been agreement, and never for long. I hope to show how far a similar objection is valid against the more abstract of the conclusions of physical science.

All science, not only the physical side of it with which we shall be concerned in this book, depends on its *concepts*. These are the ideas which receive names. They determine the questions one asks and so the answers one can get. They are more fundamental than the theories, which are stated in terms of them. Examples are motion, mass, energy, electric charge, magnetic poles, temperature, waves, particles. Some are refinements of common-sense ideas more or less directly apprehended by the senses. Others are not, but all are somehow related to experiments or experience, though many, indeed most, are not directly observable. It is a great advantage if a concept can be expressed mathematically and represented in a particular case by a number or a set of numbers, but this is not often possible in biology and even in physics there are some which cannot be so expressed, for example, the meteorological concepts of cyclones, hot and cold fronts, etc.

Even among those concepts which are capable of precise definition not all are in strict accordance with nature. They may represent approximate rough-and-ready ideas which yet can be most useful. A good example is a ray of light, thought of as a mathematical line along which light passes. Now, quite apart from the impossibility of achieving a mathematical line in the physical world, this conception only roughly agrees with facts. If one tries to get a very narrow beam of light by using fine slits or small holes to limit it, one can succeed up to a point but further narrowing of the slits or holes makes the beam spread more, not less. The concept in fact does not correspond to reality except approximately. Though this spreading and consequent bending of light has been known since the seventeenth century, and a valid explanation in terms of another concept—waves—known since the early eighteen-hundreds, rays of light continue to be used. For many laboratory purposes, and even for the laborious calculations needed to design lenses for cameras and microscopes, they are used almost exclusively. This is because they are more tractable mathematically than the subtler concept of waves and sufficiently accurate in all but a few special cases, for which allowance can be made. Though approximate, they represent a valid truth about light. In fact, the more sophisticated theories can be shown to reduce to the simple ray theory and approach it as nearly as one pleases if one works on a scale sufficiently large compared with what is called the wavelength. Since this, for ordinary light, is in the region of $\frac{2}{100{,}000}$ of an inch, rays are good enough for the design of lenses and mirrors of ordinary dimensions, except for some features of the objective lenses of microscopes when the parts of the object it is hoped to see are not much bigger than this limit.

It is characteristic of the progress of science that one concept or set of concepts can yield to another on the philosophical level without much affecting the knowledge it describes. When ray theories were abandoned as an explanation of light in favour of waves in the ether all, or nearly all, that the ray theory had taught about the design of optical instruments using lenses and mirrors remained valid, but other instruments were devised which would never have been thought of but for the wave theory. When in turn the quantum theory superseded ether theories of light, the design of neither of these two classes of instrument was affected, but the new theory is important for improving photographic plates and designing photoelectric cells.

This power of transferring detailed results from one theory to another is a great strength of science and is peculiar to it. It sounds absurd to suppose that one can alter apparently fundamental principles without much altering the detailed conclusions, but in fact this is a natural consequence of the way in which science works, namely from the details to the general. The general conclusions are rather to be thought of as the apex of a broad-based pyramid than as foundations on which the building rests. To take a different simile, the progress of science is a little like making a jig-saw puzzle. One makes collections of pieces which certainly fit together, though at first it is not clear where each group should come in the picture as a whole, and if at first one makes a mistake in placing it, this can be corrected later without dismantling the whole group.

It has sometimes been urged that the concepts and theories of science are purely human creations, not external truth. I think this view to be wrong, though of course there is a human element. It seems to me that such things are discovered rather than invented, that the scientist is more like Columbus than Arkwright, but the reader will be able to judge for himself.

One further point before examining more closely how concepts are made and used in physics: experiments and observations need an observer. The importance of the observer has become more and more realized in the last fifty years, especially in physics. Science is knowledge which, in principle at least, is public in the sense that it may be shared by many, unlike private personal experiences such as dreams or pain. This suggests a preference for statements which can be made in a form valid for large classes of possible observers. As we shall see, the Principle of Relativity is an expression of this preference.

II

THE SCIENTIFIC METHOD

and a few of the concepts resulting

MUCH has been said about the scientific method and it has received a good deal of not always well-informed homage. The scientific method is not a royal road leading to discoveries in research, as Bacon thought, but rather a collection of pieces of advice, some general some rather special, which may help to guide the explorer in his passage through the jungle of apparently arbitrary facts. Scientific research is an art, and rules for the practise of an art if they are rigid do more harm than good. In fact the sciences differ so greatly that it is not easy to find any sort of rule which applies to all without exception.

Some sciences such as physics, astronomy and genetics, can make great use of mathematics, not merely to argue about the observations that are made, but even to suggest theories. In other sciences such as botany, very little use has been made of this method so far, and it is rather difficult to see how it could be. Some sciences, such as physics and physiology lend themselves readily to experiments, in others such as astronomy and geology experiment is almost impossible and the researcher must rely on observations without the power to alter the conditions of the objects on which he is researching. In some sciences classification plays a very important part, in others it is relatively absent. In some accurate measurement is possible and important, in others it is difficult to find anything to measure which appears to have a fundamental bearing on the problem. If one tries to abstract what is common to the scientific method in all the sciences one finds indeed certain obvious requirements, such as a detached attitude, a willingness to consider all reasonable possibilities, a willingness to take pains to be exact where possible and not to allow oneself to be unduly affected by pre-conceived ideas. But these requirements are shared by other intellectual pursuits which make no claim to be scientific, such as the Law. And besides, some of them are not essential. Controversies in science have often been bitter and not always fairly conducted, but on the whole they have helped not hindered progress. Science does indeed imply accurate observation and attention to detail, an attention which can however be overdone, as in other human pursuits; selection is essential as in all arts. A scientist must be willing to alter or even abandon a favourite theory if the facts are against it. He must believe that there is some kind of rationality in nature, but he need not suppose that nature is completely determinate and indeed we shall see good reason to suppose that it is only partially so, and probably not at bottom. Nevertheless science exists by supposing that there is enough regularity in the course of events to make useful predictions possible. In history as ordinarily studied, on the other hand, this is debatable. It is by no means certain that conclusions drawn from the Middle Ages or even from the eighteenth century, however carefully made, are a useful guide to the present age. But even if they are not, this does not detract from the value of history, any more than it would from an epic. It would just mean that history is not a science.

Science, like all arts, needs imagination. The first use that had to be made of it was to see that there were things to be discovered. Very early on man realized that there were regularities in the motions of the stars which could be studied and might be important, but it took some time before he realized that there were important events on earth which could be shown to depend on definite laws. The opening up of experimental science in the Renaissance, though partly inspired by the revival of Greek learning, was, as I have suggested in the first chapter, also stimulated by the great geographical discoveries of the age which opened men's minds to the possibility of the unknown. Imagination is also needed to pick out the exciting novelty. I must again stress the importance of the trivial, but the right kind of triviality is not easy to spot.

On turning from these generalities to the single science of physics one finds that the scientific method involves frequent and careful experiments under conditions chosen to be as simple as possible, though what constitutes simple conditions is often by no means obvious and may be itself a subject for research. After the experiments are made, the crude results usually need to be analysed mathematically, using as a guide such theories or hypotheses as are available. The more general these theories can be, that is to say the less they specifically assume, the better for this primary analysis. But there always have to be some assumptions and if these assumptions are wrong the analysis may be useless. In any case in the earlier stages of a research the experiments are tentative. If the research is at all fundamental it will aim at forming concepts suggested by the experiments, then hypotheses, theories and laws are built up in terms of these concepts, these stages often need men of varying training and talents. The difference between the three terms is one of emphasis and represents not so much a difference of kind as a difference in the degree of certainty attached to them in the mind of the man who uses them.

Some concepts are deduced pretty directly from experiments, for example length, time or temperature, but in almost all cases the naïve experimental concept has to be modified. We shall examine in some detail in Chapter V how this has been done in the case of time. A somewhat similar extension has occurred in the case of temperature. By means of a mercury-in-glass thermometer one can measure something over a considerable range of conditions which can be described as 'temperature'. If very considerable care is taken with the glass and the manufacture and treatment of the thermometer, it is possible to measure this temperature with such an instrument with very considerable reproducibility from well below the freezing point of water to well above its normal boiling point. Temperatures measured by different thermometers constructed to the same specification give the same answer and we clearly have here something which has significance. On the other hand, if you compare thermometers made in different ways, for example using alcohol instead of mercury, you find that even if they are adjusted so that they read the same at the freezing and boiling points of water, they read slightly differently in between and outside these limits. To the physicist this means one of two things; either 'temperature' is not really a very fundamental quantity or what he is measuring is only an approximation to the real entity. The developments of thermodynamics in the nineteenth century showed that the latter was the case.

It is possible to define a temperature which is independent of the properties of any particular substance, and unique except for a unit, this last being arbitrary in the same sense that yards or metres are arbitrary. This concept of 'absolute temperature' was arrived at by considering the efficiency of heat engines. When an engine takes in heat, does work and rejects heat again in a cyclic process, the difference between the heat energy taken in and that rejected is equal to the energy in the form of mechanical work produced by the engine. We will forget for a moment waste in friction and such like. This is simply saying that heat and mechanical work are both forms of energy and that though one form can be changed into the other the total amount of energy is unchanged. But the fraction of the original energy which can be transformed into work is limited. This fraction is the efficiency of the engine. It never approaches 100 per cent however good the engine may be mechanically, and there is a definite limit which depends simply on the temperatures of the *source* of heat, in a steam engine the boiler, from which the heat is taken, and that of the body to which the heat is *rejected*, in a steam engine the condenser. A simple argument based on the assumed impossibility of perpetual motion shows that if such a limit exists it must be independent of the substances used. By measuring efficiencies the engine can then be used to *define* temperatures which are absolute in the sense that they do not depend on the properties of any particular substances. Actually such a scale of temperature is not very different from that measured in its limited range by a mercury-in-glass thermometer, or indeed by other thermometers based on the expansion of materials. Further, without actually constructing ideal engines it is possible to calculate corrections to the readings of some at least of these thermometers to make them fit the absolute scale.

This is rather typical of the way in which such a concept develops. One starts from the actual readings of a particular instrument, then one is able to show that these readings can be modified to give a result that no longer depends on the behaviour of a certain piece of apparatus. One has gone, as it were, beyond a particular phenomenon, in this case the expansion of mercury as it gets hot, to a concept which is much more general than this kind of experiment logically implies.

Sometimes a number of widely different experiments have to be combined to form the concept. We shall see examples of this with the electron and the nucleus. In such cases the belief that the concept as imagined corresponds to something objective, in other words has a valid existence, becomes an important hypothesis.

Certain concepts are mathematical rather than experimental in origin. One example is that of molecular chaos. The behaviour of gases can best be explained (Chapter VI) by supposing that they are composed of molecules which move with random velocities directed in all directions, the energy of their motion being a measure of the temperature of the gas. These molecules are supposed to be perpetually colliding with one another and with the walls of the vessel containing the gas. The impulse given by these collisions to the walls is what is measured as the pressure of the gas on the walls. This conception of molecular chaos, used by Maxwell and Boltzmann, was for a long time a mathematical hypothesis only. With modern experimental techniques it is indeed possible to detect the motion of molecules streaming out of a small hole in the vessel containing the gas and to find out something about their distribution, but the original conception was a mathematical one, and the kinetic theory of gases was well advanced before it was possible to detect individual motions. One is dependent on theory to elaborate concepts of this kind and to make deductions from them which can be tested by experiment.

Most concepts are approximate only—like the rays of light referred to before. In some cases the approximation is an extremely good one, especially in the rather numerous cases where it depends on the fact that atoms and molecules are very small and that there are therefore a great many of them in any piece of matter of moderate size. Take, for example, the concept of the surface of a solid as something approximating to a mathematical plane; actually such a surface at the best, and even if it is as simple as it possibly could be, consists of a number of atoms arranged in a regular pattern. The surface is not smooth in any geometrical sense of the term; if magnified the atoms would appear as lumps like a series of haycocks in a field, 'the surface' is merely an average; nor even so is it perfectly defined, for atoms do not have any sharp boundaries but rather regions in which they exert increasing forces on anything which tries to enter them. In this respect they are more like tennis balls with a nap than hard billiard balls. Nevertheless the concept of a solid surface is an extremely useful one if used with due recognition for its limitations. A few of our existing concepts may have ultimate reality but this remains to be seen, and it would be rather surprising if any of these survived without substantial modification, though they may well keep their names and much of their usefulness.

It is sometimes asserted that electrons are not 'real'. Admittedly they behave very differently from grains of sand, but it is doubtful if they are any less real than these, or than more complicated objects such as a pencil. One is so used to using the name and the idea of a body like a pencil that it requires considerable effort to realize that it is in fact a rather artificial concept, that what one really observes is a series of impressions of very different characters. Patches of colour of different brightness are observed on the retina and interpreted by a most skilful and complicated process in the brain as indicating a long solid of a hexagonal cross-section, with a conical end of a somewhat different colour from the remainder. These optical impressions are reinforced by tactile ones derived from the fingers that hold it, and by other optical impressions of black marks on paper associated with the pencil's point. From these observations one produces a concept to which one gives the name of pencil. It is difficult to see any fundamental difference between this process and that by which electrons are deduced. The relation of a concept to the reality it represents is rather like that of a flat map to a part of the earth. The map does not attempt to reproduce minor irregularities of the surface. Even if it shows contour lines it certainly ignores mole-hills. Correspondingly, the concept of physics is idealized and simplified, omitting the external distorting effects which are always there in practice. There is a further similarity in that the flat map is necessarily a distortion as applied to any considerable part of the earth surface, simply because one cannot bend a piece of paper, without folding or tearing it, so as to fit a sphere. Most concepts are, as I have said, admitted to be approximations. Further, one can have several different maps of the same bit of the earth; for example a Mercator's projection or one in which equal areas on the earth correspond to equal areas on the map. But each can be a true map in the sense that each records all the towns, mountains, rivers, etc. in the region concerned and in the right order so that those which are close together in reality are close together on the map. The map owes something to the wishes of the map maker, but it is very far from being an invention and can be right or wrong even in detail. It must not show Manchester in the middle of Spain or Oxford Circus south of Piccadilly!

Good concepts show a great power of growth beyond the original experiments that suggested them and this, I think, is one of the things that most convinces the ordinary physicist of their 'reality'. Atoms for example were suggested by Dalton at the beginning of the nineteenth century to explain the regularities which had recently been observed by chemists in the relative weights of different substances which reacted to form compounds. These experimental facts could be explained by supposing that the compounds were composed of molecules and that each molecule contained a small number of atoms of various kinds. It was a concept which contained an hypothesis going far beyond the experimental facts, and it had nearly a century to wait before evidence in its favour of a wholly different kind came forward. Since then this has accumulated quickly. The arrangements of atoms in crystalline solids are known with great accuracy from experiments with X-rays, which in a certain sense can be said to 'see' the atoms. These pack together with great regularity to form repeating patterns. Then again in organic chemistry it was gradually found that the reactions which took place indicated that the atoms in particular molecules were arranged in definite patterns. Those atoms which were near one another could then take part more readily in a joint reaction with another molecule than could atoms farther apart. The evidence, though somewhat indirect, was voluminous. Now, of course, no one would venture for a moment to doubt the reality of atoms, and in favourable circumstances they can even be seen in an electron miscroscope.

One very important group of laws in physics go under the title of 'Conservation Laws'. A conservation law really asserts that some measurable concept, e.g. energy is, at least up to a point, permanent. Conservation laws can be expressed in another way as saying that this something can neither be created nor destroyed. They become then examples of a wider group, the so-called 'principles of impotence'. These are numerous, e.g. the impossibility of making a perpetual motion machine, or the impossibility of any material object going faster than light which is the basis of 'special' relativity. Of course it is partly a matter of grammar and how one chooses to state such a law, but it is one of the striking facts of physics that so many of the most important results can so conveniently be expressed in this way—and now a word about theories.

A theory in physics is a statement, usually mathematical, of the relations between certain concepts—as Popper has pointed out, theories exist to be *dis*proved. The theory will make certain predictions as to what will be observed under certain conditions, which may be artificially produced in a laboratory or occur in natural phenomena. If these things are not observed then the theory is wrong and must be abandoned or at least altered. If they are observed the theory gets credit, and if its predictions are fulfilled over a wide and varied range the theory comes to be believed, but there is always the possibility that it may be disproved, and the near certainty that it is possible to find some special conditions to which it does not apply, conditions in which it is either unable to suggest an answer or gives the wrong one. It is never logically possible to *prove* a theory for one can never test the whole range of possible experiments which it covers. The 'uniformity of nature' is a phrase that one frequently hears. It has been well said that it was never discovered in a laboratory, for indeed laboratory apparatus has the habit of behaving in a most irrational fashion as though possessed by a Devil, and it is the task of the experimenter, and a difficult one, to tame it and to make it behave in something like a uniform manner.

But quite apart from these practical considerations there is the theoretical impossibility of ever repeating an experiment and so being in a position to say that identical experiments give identical results. In an ideal experiment one has, or hopes to have, an observer with certain pieces of apparatus, all completely isolated from the rest of the universe, for if they are not so isolated one ought to take the rest of the universe into account and the whole thing becomes impossibly complicated. In practice the experimenter will rather grudgingly admit certain generalized influences of the outside world, e.g. if the experiment is done on the earth there will be gravity; this is a nice regular kind of force which can be allowed for fairly easily and does not necessarily greatly complicate the issue. Cosmic rays are more erratic and are difficult to screen off completely. In the vast majority of experiments nobody bothers about them and for perfectly good reasons. The assumed theory of what is happening indicates that they can have no effect. But this is precisely the point; *in order to make an experiment meaningful one must have a theory as to what matters for the experiment.* Only so can you hope to make the experiment definite, let alone repeatable. When people talk of 'repeating an experiment' they mean doing something which their theory says ought to give the same result as something they have done before. Conditions never really repeat. To take one case, the modern scientist assumes that the only effects of the moon which he needs consider are its light and its tidal action, but to an astrologer of the seventeenth century, when astrology was perfectly respectable, this would have seemed a quite unwarrantable assumption; whether the moon was waxing or waning, he would say, might matter a good deal, and the same for the position of the planets. There was nothing illogical or unscientific in such beliefs until a large body of observations showed that most experiments can be made repeatable under varying conditions of the planets. This is indeed fortunate, for since the planets never all get back to exactly the same position, if their influence were always important no experiment could ever be repeated! What one can say is that it has been possible in the past to devise theories as to how certain observable events occur, which are adequate, in the sense that if the conditions required by the theory are satisfied the observed consequences will be as predicted, up to a certain degree of approximation. This shows the importance of theories, even very embryonic ones, at every stage of research; unless one has enough of a theory to know what things one can expect to matter it is impossible even to design the experiment still less to conduct it.

The simile of the map has another application. In every use of theory to predict the behaviour of an experiment or of a machine, and in every use of experiment to test a theory, a process is needed which can be described as a double translation. In terms of the map: someone has first to draw a map which represents the piece of country, and then in using the map one has to recognize the actual objects which correspond to the mountains, the streams and the woods shown. In other words the map is a translation of country into paper, its use is a translation of paper back into country. Just so with a theory, from observations and experiments in the past one constructs a theory applicable to the kind of things with which one is concerned. This theory is usually mathematical and takes the form of equations between quantities. To apply it to a particular case one puts into the equations various numbers representing the dimensions of the apparatus, weights, temperatures and anything else which the theory says is important. One turns the handle of the mathematical machine, often having to lubricate it with fairly drastic approximations and out, with luck, comes the answer. Certain symbols are found to have certain numerical values—possibly zero. Now one must translate this back into reality, into what can actually be observed. Sometimes this translation may be easy. The symbol may represent the current in a particular wire in which one has placed an ammeter, then one has only to read the ammeter to see whether it confirms or disproves the theory. In practice this only happens so simply in rather pedestrian theories; the more abstract theories usually give an answer less directly related to experiment and a subsidiary calculation is needed to connect the answer of the major theory with the reading of a dial, the angle between tracks on a photographic plate or the speed of an aeroplane as the case may be. But the principle is the same; the theory is a map which tells you what a piece of nature is like. To use it you must identify the markings on the map with things actually seen or felt.

There have been times when the quantitative sides of physics have been overstressed. Measurement and the consequent use of mathematics are immensely powerful tools but the ultimate tests are essentially qualitative. If one is designing an aeroplane it is very useful to be able to calculate its speed, but the real test of the aeroplane is to get you to New York before your friends are tired of waiting, or if it is a war machine that its pilot returns safe from the sortie and his opponent does not. The same really applies in pure science. One can always make a theory, many theories, to account for known facts, occasionally even to predict new ones. The test is aesthetic. Some theories are cumbrous, limited in scope and arbitrary. They seldom live long.

Not much has been written on the aesthetics of scientific concepts and theories; they are not quite the same as those of mathematics so well described by Hardy in that essay of genius, *A Mathematician's Apology*, but there are resemblances. In both generality counts high, very high, and so does simplicity. Anything that has obviously been put in to make the theory fit, such as particular numerical quantities, is a blemish, but this blemish may turn into a beauty if the quantity can be shown to be connected with one in an accepted theory of something else. Physics differs from mathematics in that an advance of importance is more likely to involve a new concept, even though only a secondary one. There are schools of scientific taste as of taste in other arts. To many physicists it is essential that the theory be intuitive, based on ideas which can be visualized, to others, whose turn of mind is more abstract and mathematical, this is not required; a few may even go so far as to consider it a disadvantage. Strict definition of the concepts and precise logical arguments then take the place of intuition. This is all right for those problems which can be solved completely, for the many which cannot one is completely baffled, while the more intuitive theories usually give one some rough idea of what the answer will be, especially if one has had a fair amount of experience of similar but easier problems which can in fact be solved. In physics, as in mathematics, it is a great beauty if a theory can bring together apparently very different phenomena and show that they are closely connected; or even different aspects of the same thing, as when Maxwell showed that an improvement in the laws of electricity, which added to their generality, also made it possible to explain light in terms of electricity and deduce its velocity correctly from purely electrical measurements; or when Newton showed that the moon is falling like an apple.

Beauty in experiment depends firstly on devising an experiment which goes straight to the heart of the problem and asks a question which nature is prepared to answer. In the actual experiment one admires economy of effort by which no more is attempted than is strictly necessary for success, and at a lower level detailed ingenuity. As in all artistic achievements the aesthetic qualities must be supported by technical ability, or the experiment will simply fail to get any answer at all. This is the side of experimental work most obvious to the young researcher.

JAMES CLERK MAXWELL

JAMES CLERK MAXWELL came of sound Lowland stock. The Clerks of Penicuik in Midlothian were an old respected family who came from Aberdeenshire in the days of Queen Mary. The name of Maxwell had come into the family a few generations before from the female side; James's grandfather did not bear it. With the name went an estate of which some land in Kirkudbrightshire, with the house of Glenhair, remained when James was born. Here he spent his childhood and returned in middle life. His mother died when he was eight; his father, with whom he was great friends, was a man of sound common sense, with a keen interest in all useful processes. He encouraged the boy in working with his hands and in drawing.

James went to school in Edinburgh, staying with relatives, and then at sixteen to the University. He was lucky in going to one of the few universities where practical work was even then being done in physics, at least by Professor Forbes with whom he became very friendly. He learnt to turn, and made himself a 'devil-on-two-sticks', as the later diabolo was then called. The spinner was a heavy object of black wood. At the age of nineteen he went to Cambridge and read mathematics, for in those days physics was only beginning to be a recognized subject and the approach to it was through mathematics.

Maxwell is known today to the student of physics for two things, his work on the kinetic theory and his electromagnetic equations. In fact he did much more, including some experimental work, but his theoretical work was greater than his experimental.

He did not originate the kinetic theory, the idea that a gas is composed of vast numbers of particles dashing about in all directions, striking one another and the walls of the vessels containing them; this goes back to the seventeenth century. But he was the first to see the possibility of extracting order from the chaos. He proved mathematically that just *because* the motions and the collisions are random the distribution of energy among the particles is definite and can be calculated. For example, the number of particles with more than twice the average kinetic energy is 8·3% of the whole and the number with more than three times is only 2·5% of the whole. Out of irregular chaos comes law. What is perhaps even more surprising is that the law does not depend on the nature of the particles or on the forces they exert on each other. Within certain limits it is a fundamental property of matter in equilibrium. Kinetic theory is the one part of nineteenth-century physics in which the idea of probability is needed, the idea which now bulks so large. Maxwell was aware of this peculiar character of the theory. He invented a 'demon' who is supposed to sit by a door in a wall separating two vessels of gas at the same temperature. Whenever an extra fast molecule comes from the right he opens the door and also if an extra slow one comes from the left. Otherwise he keeps it closed. Since temperature measures average energy, the temperature of the gas on the left of the wall will rise, that on the right will fall. This is quite contrary to the principles of thermodynamics according to which the creation of a *difference* of temperature such as this is only possible if mechanical, chemical, or other outside source of energy is avoidable. The demon does it by intelligence only, the force he has to use could be negligible.

Maxwell's equations are a combined statement of the basic laws of electricity and of magnetism. They have stood the test of time remarkably well. Though they have been reinterpreted to suit the quantum theory and provide for electrons they remain indispensable. Modern theoretical physicists are no respecters of persons, still less of their theories, but even they hesitate to tamper with Maxwell's equations. It comes as a shock to discover that Maxwell arrived at them as the result of considerations which involved a complicated model with rotating vortices representing magnetic force separated by particles which played the part of idle pinions in a train of gears, and also functioned as a kind of electricity! Nowadays, if presented with such a thing one would take a single look at it and then put it firmly in the waste-paper basket. Maxwell discarded almost all the mechanism before his final draft; the result was a theory that his contemporaries found difficult and arbitrary. It was slow in being accepted but attracted a few people, such as my father and Heaviside, who helped to make it widely known. But not till Hertz found his waves experimentally did it become unquestioned.

Maxwell was the first Cavendish Professor of Experimental Physics in the new laboratory built by the generosity of the Duke of Devonshire (himself a former second Wrangler). It was not indeed there when he was appointed and it was some time before he was able to get to work. Maxwell spent a good deal of his efforts in the purchase of apparatus, the money being supplied by the Duke, and was able to declare that the laboratory had 'all the instruments required in the present state of Science'. Since Maxwell said so, it must have been so, but I remember my father saying that it certainly could not have been said of any time later.

Maxwell spent a very substantial part of his time at Cambridge in editing the Cavendish papers, a pious duty. Henry Cavendish, an eighteenth-century member of the family of the Duke, had been an eccentric nobleman of genius. He had published only two papers, both for special reasons, but had left a vast mass of material. Maxwell was able to show that he had in fact anticipated most of the discoveries in electrostatics of the fifty years after his death. Maxwell's edition of his papers is a model for the historians of science, but one cannot help grudging the time it cost.

But you must not suppose that Maxwell was another of those solemn Victorians. Perhaps they were not as solemn as we think, but certainly that is the last adjective one should apply to him. His sense of fun was innate and bubbled out in all sorts of ways—in sketches to illustrate his letters home, in comic verse, though he wrote some that were serious. His parody of *Coming through the Rye* has lived:

Gin a body meet a body
Flyin' through the air,
Gin a body hit a body,
Will it fly? and where?
Ilka impact has its measure,
Ne'er a ane hae I,
Yet a' the lads they measure me,
Or, at least, they try.

Gin a body meet a body
Altogether free,
How they travel afterwards
We do not always see.
Ilka problem has its method
By analytics high;
For me, I ken na ane o' them,
But what the waur am I?

His fun even touched his physics. Who but he would have called his molecular doorman a demon? But Maxwell's demon he is and remains.

He died on 5 November 1879. There are few men about whose character there is such unanimity. He must have been an exceptionally lovable person, both the recorded facts and the remembered impressions agree. He was a good son, a devoted husband, a loyal and understanding friend. To all human relationships he brought rich gifts of unselfishness and kindness. He was a deeply religious man, very reticent except in those rare circumstances when he felt it his duty not to be or when he was with close intimates. From the letters in Lewis Campbell's *Life* it is clear that his religion was the result of deep and careful thought; it came from intellectual conviction as well as from something much more.

III

WHAT ARE THINGS MADE OF?

1. ATOMS

If one considers ordinary material things—a piece of wood or of stone, a nail or the water in a bucket, and asks what they are ultimately made of, the possible answers fall into two broad classes. One can say that, though the wood is obviously composed of fibres and the stone of grains of sand somehow stuck together, this is merely their gross structure and that on proper dissection one would find several homogeneous substances each uniform and capable of subdivision to a degree only limited by the fineness of the tools at one's disposal. But one could also say, at least since Leucippus, first of the atomists, had this idea some time in the fifth century B.C., that all these bodies are composed of very large numbers of small hard bodies—atoms—which might or might not be of more than one kind for any one piece of matter. Modern science is overwhelmingly on the side of the atomists, but the concept of atom has changed a lot since the days of Leucippus, mostly in the last seventy years.

Until the end of the last century it was still possible, though getting difficult, to regard the idea of atoms as being indeed a useful hypothesis, but one which might be discarded and should be used with caution. It was the purists for scientific rigour who took this view. Chemists had been using atoms cheerfully for most of the century. The cautious view became merely pedantic when it became possible to observe in several ways individual atoms and parts of atoms. That there should be detachable parts of atoms is a substantial modification of the original idea which seemed very revolutionary when J. J. Thomson first produced compelling evidence for it in a series of experiments published in the two years from May 1897. Actually, the successors of Leucippus, Democritus and Epicurus, specifically discussed in some detail the 'parts' of their atoms, but they were not supposed to be separable. Though by derivation 'atom' means 'uncuttable' the word has wisely been kept: not merely would a change have been excessively inconvenient, but the modern atom fills the place in theory taken by the atoms of Epicurus much more nearly than do any of the more recently discovered constituents such as electrons or protons.

It would take the whole of this book to give a comprehensible account of the evidence which has lead to the modern concepts of molecules, atoms, electrons, and of nuclei and their constituents. I shall only attempt to give the evidence in two special cases, and for the rest simply state the conclusions.

There are 90 species of atoms normally present on the earth. Analysis of the light from the sun and stars shows that most of these, but no others, occur in space. Each of these has a name and is called an 'element'. Examples are: hydrogen, carbon, oxygen, sodium, aluminium, sulphur, chlorine, iron, copper, tin, gold, radium. In most cases the atoms of an element are of more than one kind forming several 'subspecies'. Each subspecies is known as an 'isotope' and is usually denoted by a whole number which is an approximate measure of its relative weight. Thus 'carbon 13' is the name of a rare isotope of carbon, the majority of the atoms of carbon have weight 12, but one in a hundred are heavier and weigh about 13 units. Of the 90 elements only about 30 are really common and many are very rare, but even these are increasingly finding technical uses and few are now entirely unused. Nature was ahead of man in this, for quite a number of the rare elements have been found to be necessary for certain kinds of life. It is well known that some Australian pastures need the addition of cobalt, and it is now believed that absence of selenium is the cause of a disease in sheep.

Among these 90 elements are some which are radioactive, radium itself is a good example. The atoms of these elements are unstable and break up into others, thus half the atoms in a piece of radium break up in 1,590 years. Yet the number of radium atoms on the earth hardly changes. They are replaced by atoms produced by the break-up of yet heavier ones, which in their turn some from others, and ultimately from uranium or thorium which, though also unstable, have so long a life that a large fraction is still left of the stock with which the earth started perhaps 4,000 million years ago. Atoms heavier than uranium can be made artificially, they are all more or less unstable. One of them, plutonium, has become of great military importance as a bomb material. In addition, all elements can have radioactive (and therefore unstable) isotopes and the preparation of these has now become commercially important.

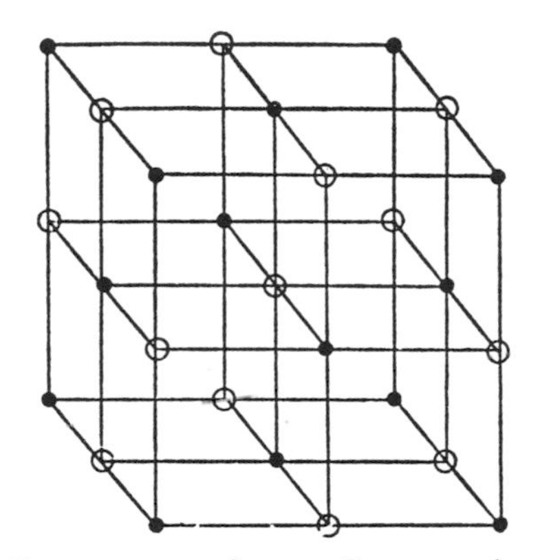

FIG. 2.—STRUCTURE OF SODIUM CHLORIDE (*common salt*)

The solid dots may represent the centres of sodium atoms, the circles those of chlorine atoms, but if the structure is extended indefinitely it can be seen that it is reciprocal, each dot being surrounded by six circles and each circle by six dots.

All substances contain some impurities, even the germanium and silicon specially prepared to make transistors have a few parts per billion (thousand million), but neglecting traces, reasonably pure substances fall roughly into two categories, elements and compounds. In an element—again neglecting traces of impurities—all the atoms belong to one species, though only in very special cases to one subspecies. For example among metals, copper, silver, gold and iron are elements and so are graphite (carbon) sulphur and iodine among non-metals. On the other hand water, salt, sulphuric acid, acetone are typical compounds. In a normally constituted compound there are groups of atoms called molecules, each group being identical. For example, each molecule of steam contains two atoms of hydrogen and one of oxygen and is written H_2O. Molecules are most clearly defined when the substance is vaporized. In liquids they may stick together in groups of two or three, and in many solids there is no true molecule, only a regular arrangement of atoms. For example, in common salt there are equal numbers of sodium and chlorine atoms so arranged that each sodium atom has six chlorine atoms arranged round it at the corners of an imaginary octahedron of which the sodium is the centre, and conversely each chlorine has six sodium atoms similarly arranged around it.

Yet in every case of a true compound atomic proportions are kept, so many of one kind to so many of another. Compounds may contain several kinds of atoms but always in these integral proportions. This law of integral proportions by number of atoms is indeed virtually the definition of a true compound. Solutions, such as that of salt in water, are intermediate in certain respects between the true compounds and crude mixtures such as old-fashioned black gunpowder, made by mixing finely powdered nitre, sulphur and carbon. In the mixture individual specks of the mixed substances can be seen under a miscroscope, but however much a drop of brine is magnified it will appear a homogeneous liquid. In this respect it is like a compound between the salt and water, but it is not a true compound since the salt may be present in the water in any proportion up to the maximum which the brine will take up. By contrast some solids, such as sodium carbonate (washing soda), are true compounds of the salt with water, in the case of washing soda, one molecule of sodium carbonate to ten of water. Some alloys, such as those of silver with gold, are like solutions, others are definite compounds.

A very important class of compounds is the organic. This term was used originally to denote compounds derived from tissues once living. Now it merely means compounds containing carbon. Nowadays the commonest starting point is crude oil, which though it may have been derived ages ago from marine animals has lost all traces of its origin. Some organic compounds such as marsh gas with five atoms per molecule and methanol with six are fairly simple, but many of those most important in living matter are of great complexity. Haemoglobin and myoglobin, two proteins whose structures are now being unravelled by Perutz and Kendrew in Cambridge have respectively about 10,000 and 2,500 atoms each. Yet apparently each of these atoms, which are arranged in subgroups, has its definite place in the molecule and the exchange in the blood of an animal or man of one of these subgroups for another closely similar, but with one or two atoms changed, can cause a fatal disease.

Proteins are the most complex molecules yet understood, perhaps the most complex ones which are essential to life, but myriads of less complicated molecules have been studied, analysed and synthesized. There is no essential difference between the compounds in living bodies and the rest of the world except for the greater complexity of some of the living molecules. In the course of their studies chemists have found not only how many atoms of which kinds constitute the molecule of a particular substance but how these atoms are arranged. In most cases the molecules are built up out of the atoms like a building out of bricks, but in a few cases there are moving parts so that the molecule alternates between two configurations, rather as a soft rubber ball can be deformed into a bowl and then spring out again. Often the arrangement of the atoms has been confirmed by finding how they scatter X-rays.

In all this work with atoms in molecules and crystals one cannot help being struck by the matter-of-fact—almost commonplace—way in which they behave. They do really stack together —if not like cannon balls—at least like tennis balls. Each tends to occupy a fairly definite space, they can indeed be compressed a little, but if the compression is much it affects the stability of the structure, be it crystal or organic molecule. Unfortunately this commonsense behaviour is not followed by electrons as we shall see later, and even atoms can behave queerly in special circumstances.

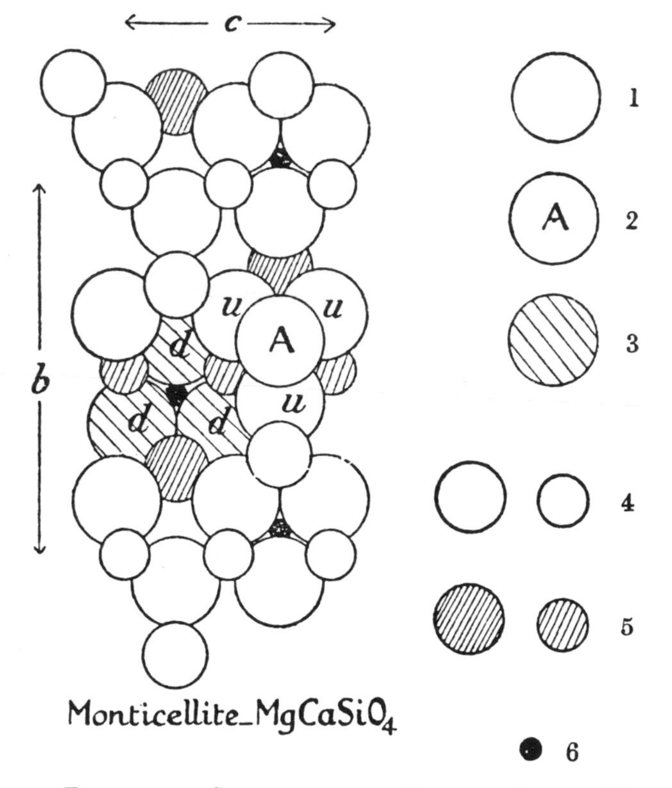

FIG. 3. ELEMENT OF STRUCTURE OF A TYPICAL SILICATE MINERAL SHOWING HOW THE LARGER OXYGEN ATOMS ACCOMMODATE THE SMALLER CALCIUM MAGNESIUM AND SILICON ATOMS IN BETWEEN THEM

1. Oxygen atoms lying nearly in the plane of the paper. 2. Oxygen atoms in a plane above that of the paper, included to show tetrahedral groups. 3. Oxygen atoms below the plane of the paper. 4. *Ca Mg* atoms lying on the oxygen layer marked (1). 5. *Ca Mg* atoms lying below the oxygen layer. 6. *Si* atoms.

The discovery of the electron marks an epoch in physics and the process is sufficiently typical of great discoveries to be worth describing in some detail. Two separate ideas met and fused in the years following 1897. One goes back to the earliest stages of

Greek thought, before Leucippus even; it is the idea of a universal element of which all things are made. The other grew slowly in the nineteenth century. It is the idea that electricity is divided into natural units. After much vague talk about 'effluvia', eighteenth-century science settled down to the idea that electricity is a fluid, or possibly two fluids. The normal method of producing electricity was then by friction. Later, when Galvani and Volta discovered the electric current produced by chemical action in primary cells—in principle the same as the dry batteries now used in torches—the chemical effects of electricity came into prominence. Faraday in the eighteen-thirties studied the chemical changes produced when a current goes through solutions of salts of various kinds such as are used for electroplating. He called the process electrolysis. He measured the amounts of gases and solids produced at the two plates, called electrodes, where the current enters and leaves the solution. He discovered simple relations between the relative weights of substances produced by a given current in a given time and the relative weights of the same substances which combined together to form compounds. The current split the compound up into two component parts—one component going to each electrode, and the amount broken up was proportional to the amount of electricity which had passed, i.e. to the product of current and time. It looked as though compounds were broken up molecule by molecule, each molecule into two parts and each of the two broken parts of each molecule bearing a charge either of 'positive' or of 'negative' electricity.* The motion of these charges would then constitute the current through the solution, just as the motion of a number of drops of water would constitute a flow or current of water; this was indeed generally believed. But if so, the relations Faraday had found between the current flowing and the rate at which materials were produced at the electrodes implied that the charges on the positively charged halves of most molecules are the same. The same result holds for the negative halves. In certain cases the charge on either half is exactly two, or exactly three, times the

* The terms positive and negative electricity are to be considered here as merely names for the two kinds of electricity.

normal amount. These 'half molecules' are sometimes single atoms, sometimes groups of atoms; both single atoms and groups can have either the normal or multiple charge. In any case, the mass of each half molecule is associated with a particular charge. The ratio (charge divided by mass) is characteristic of the kind of atom or group of atoms. To us now this seems very strong evidence for electric charges being in units, and if in units for these dissolved atoms and groups of atoms why not always? Though this possibility was realized it was not given much weight. The very great successes of nineteenth-century physics were mostly achieved by ideas of continuity, atoms were left to the chemists. Faraday himself and Maxwell after him thought more about what is going on in the space between two electrified bodies than about the nature of the 'charges' which these bodies were said to possess. Charges, on this view, had a rather doubtful reality, they might turn out only to be a name for the way in which the electrical processes in the ether attached themselves to matter, and so became observable.

However, towards the end of the century there was a change of temper. The great Dutch physicist, Lorentz, put forward a theory of electricity in which charge was more prominent, he used the word 'electron' which Johnstone Stoney, who emphasized the importance of the evidence from electrolysis, had invented in 1891. Lorentz also associated a mass with the charge, J. J. Thomson having shown ten years before that a charge would automatically produce an extra mass which would be *greater* the smaller the body which carried the charge. So far there was no experimental evidence.

The other half of the story is the history of cathode rays. These are produced when an electric current goes through gas at a suitable low pressure. Usually the gas was in a glass bulb with metal electrodes sealed in carrying the current in and out. From the cathode, as the electrode conventionally 'negative' is called, streams out a bundle of rays faintly visible in the gas and producing a bright patch of fluorescence when they reached the glass. They normally go in straight lines but can easily be bent if a magnet is brought near the tube. A tolerably good vacuum is needed, and their discovery in the middle of the nineteenth century was due to improvements in air pumps.

In the early nineties a considerable controversy was raging as to their nature. One school of thought, strongest in Britain and France, thought that they were particles shot off from the cathode by electric force; the other, strongest in Germany, that they were a new form of waves. It took till 1927 to prove that both were right, but at the moment we are concerned with the nineties.

The evidence was fairly evenly balanced. Hertz had recently discovered the radio waves predicted by Maxwell, and waves were in the air both metaphorically and literally. Lenard at Heidelberg had sent the rays into the atmosphere by covering part of the tube by a very thin metal window. They went through this without injuring it, though it was free from holes and allowed no leak into the vacuum of the tube. This seemed hard to explain if the rays were particles, for no one then considered anything smaller than atoms.

On the other hand Perrin at Paris had shown that if the rays were caught just before striking the wall, in a suitable metal cup, they gave it a negative charge. This agreed with the magnetic deflection. which was in the direction and of the kind to be expected from a stream of negatively electrified particles. But Hertz had sent a beam of the rays between two parallel metal plates in the gas and then connected the plates to the poles of an electric battery. Nothing happened. Now electrified particles ought to be pulled sideways by the electric force between the plates and so deflected.

J. J. Thomson made a slight improvement on Perrin's experiment by showing that it worked even if the rays had been magnetically deflected. He also measured the magnetic deflection and showed that it was independent of the nature of the residual gas in the tube and of the metal of which the cathode was made, if the voltage was kept the same. This could favour particles, if the particles were universal. 'J.J.' was impressed by this universal character of the rays. Lenard had found that equal absorption of the rays was caused by equal masses of matter whatever its composition. This seemed quite unlike an atomic effect, which should depend on chemistry, but it would fit with a particle—or *corpuscle* as Thomson called it—brought to rest by colliding with many similar corpuscles in the matter, the same in kind for all substances and proportional in number to the mass traversed. Then by improving the vacuum he was able to explain Hertz's result, the strongest argument against the rays being electrified particles. In a good vacuum the rays *are* in fact deflected by an electric field. Hertz's absence of result was due to a secondary effect. The rays in going through the residual gas had split up some of the molecules much as they might have been divided in a solution, with a charge on each half. These charged ions, as they are called, are attracted to the electrified plates, form a layer near them and partly or wholly neutralize the electrical effect even a short distance away. Convinced that the rays were particles he then measured by two methods the ratio of the mass to the electrical charge. This quantity was estimated at about the same time by other workers but their methods either only gave limits or involved assumptions which were hard to justify. His methods gave reasonably concordant results and showed that whatever the gas or cathode the ratio of charge to mass was about a thousand times more than Faraday had found for hydrogen in electrolysis. Hydrogen, the lightest element, is that for which the ratio is largest. The second of Thomson's two methods used the recently discovered deflection by electric fields. This apparatus incidentally was afterwards developed into the 'cathode ray oscilloscope', probably the device most widely used by workers in electronics today.

Thomson concluded that his corpuscles were much lighter than any known atom and were a universal constituent of matter. A few months before, the young Dutchman, Zeeman, had repeated an experiment of Faraday's, the last Faraday ever did. This was to examine the light from a sodium flame in a spectroscope and see if a strong magnetic field applied to the flame made any difference to the two fine yellow lines close together into which the spectroscope analyses the light. Faraday had seen no change. Zeeman with a more powerful magnet and better technique saw the lines grow fuzzy. Closer examination showed other changes

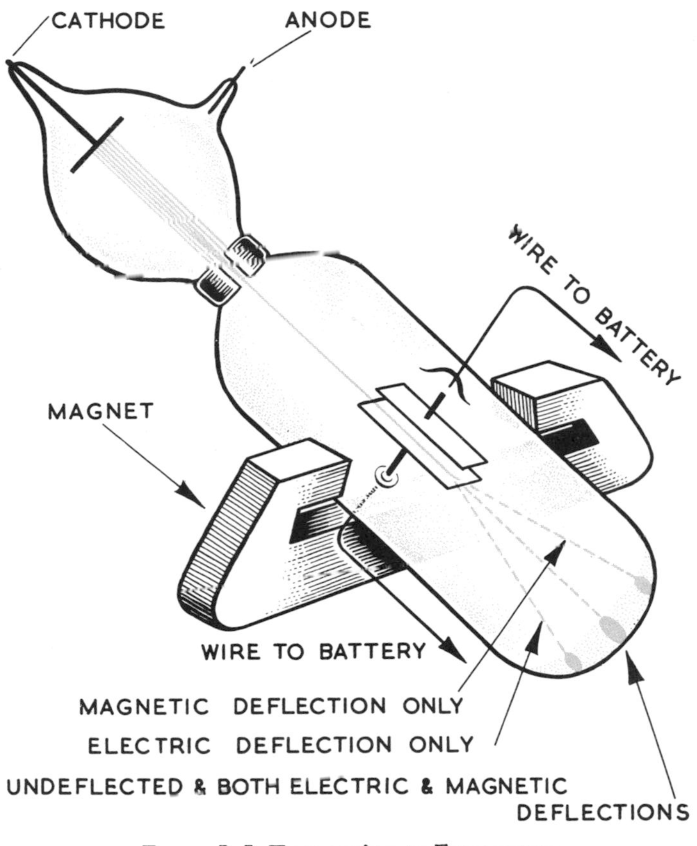

FIG. 4. J. J. THOMSON'S E/M EXPERIMENT

The electric field between the plates is found from the voltage of the battery. The field of the magnet is measured in an auxiliary experiment. The velocity of the rays is found by balancing the two deflections.

in the light. Zeeman consulted Lorentz who explained the effect on his electron theory. Assuming that electrons were the source of the light he could calculate from Zeeman's observations the ratio of mass to charge for the electrons. It came out roughly the same as for the cathode rays.

Even with this support from a wholly different branch of

physics the hypothesis was far from proved and in fact few physicists believed it. But evidence rapidly accumulated. The small ratio of mass to charge might mathematically speaking have been explained as readily by large charge as by small mass. Other ions were known in gases. Thomson and Rutherford had proved the year before, shortly after X-rays were discovered, that the conductivity which X-rays caused in gases was due to ions. C. T. R. Wilson had discovered that artificial clouds condense preferentially on these ions, one drop on each. Thomson used this result to measure the charge on an X-ray ion. The result was about that expected for the Faraday ions in solutions, but their charge could only be roughly estimated. A few months later Townsend was able to show by an indirect but accurate method that the charges for Faraday and X-ray ions are in fact the same. However, cathode rays are not X-rays though they produce them. It was hardly possible to measure the charge on an individual cathode ray; it would not be too easy now, but there might be other sources of corpuscles. Two other ways were known by which negative electricity could escape into a vacuum, from a hot wire and when ultra-violet light shone on a zinc plate. Thomson measured the mass/charge ratio for the carriers of the negative electricity in each case and found it the same as for cathode rays. In the second case he was also able to measure the charge. It agreed with the others, and the proof was complete of charged particles much lighter than any atom and derived from a great variety of substances.

One common constituent of matter had been discovered. The Greek idea of a universal element had proved true. This discovery well exemplifies the varied demands of research in physics. A physicist must not merely have an insight into nature of a semi-intuitive kind but he must be able to assess experimental evidence which must not always be taken at its face value. If he has a theory he must be able to put it into mathematical form and devise an apparatus which will give a numerical result that can be compared with his theory without introducing additional assumptions, or if this is not possible, with the minimum of such assumptions. But with all this, success or failure may depend on his ability to make improvements in experimental technique which might not seem to a looker-on as of much importance. After all, it might have been said, the vacuum used by Hertz and others was quite adequate for producing cathode rays—why bother to improve it?

Since that time electrons have been the most basic of the concepts in terms of which matter is explained, but with the passing of time the concept has greatly changed. Some of these changes will be described in Chapter IX. I will pass briefly over the period between the discovery of electrons and that of atomic nuclei by Rutherford, the other discovery that I shall attempt to describe in this chapter in any detail.

It early became apparent that though an electron had a mass less than $\frac{1}{1000}$ that of even the lightest atom (in fact about $\frac{1}{1838}$) there are not nearly 1,000 electrons in an atom. Three rather rough methods of estimating that number showed that it is of the order of the conventional atomic weight of an atom. Actually it is rather under one half: thus carbon, with an atomic weight (for its commonest isotope) of 12 has 6 electrons; uranium, whose commonest isotope is 238 has 92 electrons. It follows that electrons only supply a small fraction of the mass of an atom. Further, electrons have an electric charge of the kind conventionally called 'negative'. Since like charges repel, matter composed only of electrons would burst with enormous violence—indeed could never exist. There must be a 'positively' charged constituent to neutralize the electrons and this perhaps might supply all or much of the missing mass. Its discovery was not as dramatic as that of the electron, but evidence gradually accumulated which pointed to the residue of a hydrogen atom when one electron was removed—and there was good reason to suppose that this lightest atom had in fact only one electron. Anyhow no one had found a lighter positive charge than this and the chief difficulty was that the weights found by the chemists for the atoms of elements were not whole number multiples of the weight of a hydrogen atom. This difficulty arose mostly because isotopes had not then been discovered and the chemical weights were an average for the different isotopes of an element, which are virtually inseparable by chemical means. Thus chlorine has a chemical atomic weight of about 35·5, hydrogen being unity; it contains atoms weighing nearly 35 and others less numerous weighing nearly 37, the average taking account of the relative numbers in the mixture comes to 35·5 which is what the chemists had found.

It was quite uncertain, even assuming that the mass and positive charge were due to hydrogen residues—which I shall in future call protons—how either these or the electrons were distributed in the volume of an atom.

J. J. THOMSON

HIS work in discovering the electron has been described. It was followed up by investigations by himself and his now numerous pupils on such matters as the number of electrons in the atom, the mechanism of the conduction of electricity through gases, the scattering of X-rays and the ionization they produce, the theory of metallic conduction and many allied matters.

About 1905 he turned to the study of positive rays. I shall describe in the note on Aston how this led to the discovery of the isotopes of ordinary elements, but it is worth mentioning for another reason. By the use of deflections caused by electric and magnetic fields (Fig. 5) he was able to analyse these rays (which occur in a discharge tube behind the cathode if it is pierced by holes or a tube) to prove what had indeed been suspected, that they are a mixed stream of (usually) positively charged atoms and molecules, to separate the particles of different mass (more accurately, of different charge/mass ratio) and to show them as curved lines on a photographic plate. The fact that these lines were sharp to within instrumental limits showed for the first time that atoms of one kind have really the same mass, and that atomic weight is not just a statistical mean, as the weight of the population of a country would be, but definite for a given group. Aston was to prove the 'group' to be those of the same isotope, not as before supposed all those of the same element. Incidentally,

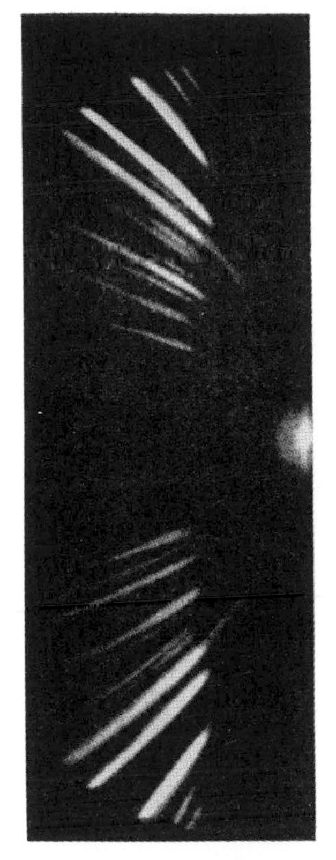

FIG. 5. POSITIVE RAYS

Pattern made on a photographic plate by positive rays which have been deflected horizontally by an electric field and vertically by a magnetic one. The pattern is doubled because the magnetic field has been reversed half-way through the exposure. Each parabolic arc represents one value of e/m and one kind of atom or molecule. The three brightest on each side correspond to the atoms of oxygen, nitrogen and carbon with unit charge. Weaker arcs further from the centre correspond to some of these with double charges. The gas was the residual air with an impurity of hydrocarbon from the grease used for the glass taps.

this technique is now used extensively in the analysis of the products of cracking crude oil, which would have given J.J. much pleasure as he always stressed its value in chemical analysis.

Though J.J. was trained as a mathematician, he did much theoretical work and retained his skill in mathematical analysis to an advanced age. His habit of thought was essentially physical. Mathematics was only a tool not an inspiration—this came from visualized physical ideas, sketched on the back of an envelope. (*On*velope he called it in what, I suppose, was Manchester usage in his boyhood.) He was attracted by the idea of lines of force, which had been suggested to Faraday by the appearance of iron filings near a magnet and developed by Maxwell. He was inclined to believe in the physical reality of both magnetic and electric lines of force. Present-day theory regards these as merely convenient mathematical fictions, but they certainly are convenient and are proving especially so today in the study of how very hot gases can be contained by magnetic fields so as to produce a fusion nuclear reaction, the problem of Zeta.

He believed strongly in the importance of the right approach to a problem; he called it, more simply, 'getting hold of the right end of the stick'. For this reason he disagreed with the usual practice of going away and reading up the literature when faced by a new problem. He advised instead thinking it over for oneself and making some sort of independent attack. Later one should read what others have done; done too soon this implants ideas not easily eradicated and makes an original approach unlikely.

It would be wrong to think of J.J. as the recluse type of scientist, though he tended a little that way in his last years. In his great days he was the leader of a group of free researchers, the first man, at least in Britain, to form a school of this kind. Rutherford and Townsend were his first two research students from outside Cambridge, but the number soon grew and the Cavendish became a world-centre for physics, giving professors to most of the English-speaking world. Most laboratory teas trace their descent to the Cavendish where he invited research students to meet for it in his room, and discussed everything but physics.

Then in 1917 he was appointed Master of Trinity and when the war ended gave up his chair to Rutherford, retaining only a little space for his own work and that of a few pupils.

The Master of a Cambridge College is in a curious position, with little power, but a good deal of influence. J.J. had his views on how things ought to be done, but he had little love of power over men. Instead he had a wide interest in what men did—men rather than women who, with a few exceptions, he found rather boring. There was hardly anyone he could not talk to, and few subjects to which he could not contribute a new or at least a vivid point of view. I must except music, for which he had a definite distaste, which he attributed to being told off in early youth to take visitors to Halle concerts. He had a great interest in games, and though he was but a mediocre performer, knew what had been going on in Cambridge sport for half a century.

Gardening was his great love, but he did not do much with his hands; he was, in fact, surprisingly clumsy with them, and though he could diagnose the faults of an apparatus with uncanny accuracy it was just as well not to let him handle it. Most of his experiments were set up for him by his assistant, Everett, though he took the actual readings. He was terribly untidy with papers, but to balance this wrote a neat and really beautiful hand—his one manual dexterity. He had a bad habit of not answering letters. I could never be sure how far this was policy—it was sometimes very successful—and how far unwillingness to break into a train of thought. He had great power of concentration; if he was working it was no good speaking to him; he just didn't hear, which was curiously disconcerting. I have heard him say that the best way to conquer a difficult problem is first to study it hard and then to go away and think of something else, when one got back the solution often fell out. All the same it took a lot to make him break off.

He had a great sense of humour, but not when it was a question of physics; that was too serious. The two great virtues of a physicist in his eyes were originality and enthusiasm, and he ranked men accordingly, with a preference for enthusiasm as the indispensible motive force.

F. W. ASTON

ASTON'S work as a physicist is outstanding for two things, his personal skill as a maker and designer-user of apparatus and his faith in following through to a successful conclusion a belief based on good but inconclusive evidence. It came about like this. Soddy had found that some of the many radioactive bodies which are formed by the spontaneous breaking up of the elements uranium and thorium, though quite different in the rays they produced, were inseparable chemically. He called them 'isotopes', regarding them, correctly, as atomic subspecies. This was before Rutherford had discovered the nucleus. At about this time J. J. Thomson was working with his 'positive rays'. He was looking for the positive equivalent of the electron but found nothing lighter than a positively charged hydrogen atom, now called a proton. He found, as I have said, a variety of other atomic and molecular species. By 1910 Aston, who had been trained as a chemist and worked three years with a brewer, had turned his interest to the physics of gas discharge. In that year J.J., using a grant from the Royal Institution for an assistant, asked him to come and help with the positive ray work. Without going into details of the apparatus, it separated the different kinds of charged particles in the beam of rays recording them each as a parabolic arc on a photographic plate in order of their masses (more exactly, their ratio of mass to charge). When the gas neon, one of the group of inert gases found as a consequence of Rayleigh's discovery of argon, was in the discharge two otherwise unknown parabolae appeared. The mass of the stronger fitted reasonably with the mass of 20·2 to be expected for a charged atom of neon. The other had a mass of about 22 and was a mystery. It appeared definitely associated with neon and did not appear unless neon was in the tube. There were two plausible explanations, not to mention others less probable. The gas neon might be composed of two kinds of atoms of weight 20 and 22 but otherwise nearly identical properties; if so they could be examples of Soddy's isotopes but this time part of a normal non-radioactive element. It would break the normal sequence of chemical properties in the elements arranged in order of atomic weight to assume 22 is just another inert gas with mass near that of neon. The alternative was to suppose that the 22 parabola was due to the molecule of a compound, not to a bare atom, presumably the molecule NeH_2 which would give the right mass. To this came the obvious objection that neon is chemically inert and does not form compounds. This sounds conclusive, but in fact J.J. had just found in the rays compounds then unknown to chemists and in particular hydrides. True, none of these had so far contained inert gases, but perhaps. . . !

Aston set to work to prove his hunch that neon has isotopes by separating them by physical means. Separation of isotopes is now a great industry. The plant at Oak Ridge, Tennessee, for separating the isotopes of uranium is said to consume more electrical power than the whole of France. In those days nothing was known. He first tried fractional distillation of liquid neon. This failed, as we now know it was bound to do so. Aston then tried diffusing the gas through pipe clay. The theory of the diffusion of gases through small holes is physically simple and well understood. The lighter gas diffuses faster to an extent which can be calculated. Aston, after thousands of operations got a small positive effect, measured on a delicate balance of his own devising which determined the densities of the samples of gas. Though definite the effect was small enough for argument to be possible.

Then came the war. Aston went to work at the Royal Aircraft Factory at Farnborough where he returned to chemistry and studied things like the dope used to stretch the canvas that covered the wooden wings of the aircraft of those days. He joined an unofficial civilian mess in a house called Chudleigh with a number of other scientists including Lord Cherwell (then Professor Lindemann) and myself. I remember well the arguments between Aston and Lindemann, who was sceptical as to neon isotopes. Lindemann always won, for he was a much better theoretical physicist than Aston; but next evening Aston came back undaunted. In the end he partly convinced Lindemann, and they published a joint paper on possible methods of separating isotopes.

When the war ended Aston returned to the Cavendish with an independent studentship and built, with his own hands, a much better diffusion apparatus, mechanized so that the operation of diffusion could be repeated a very large number of times. It gave a completely zero result, not even the small separation of the pre-war model. Most men would have given up, for the theory seemed sound and the apparatus worked well mechanically. The fault, we now know, was due to insufficient mixing of the gas waiting to diffuse, so that while to begin with the lighter atoms went through faster, as they should, the layer of gas next the pipe-clay soon became depleted of light atoms and the proportion of heavy atoms going through increased.

Aston guessed something of the sort, but instead of trying to get better mixing wisely tried an entirely different line. The atomic weight of neon as measured by density is 20·2; this density could be the result of mixing about 10% of an isotope of weight 22 with 90% of one of weight 20. It could also simply mean that all neon atoms weigh 20·2. If one could determine *exactly* the weight of the neon forming the strongest parabola one could distinguish and settle the matter, but J.J.'s parabola apparatus was not accurate enough. Aston thought up a new ingenious arrangement of electric and magnetic fields capable of much greater accuracy and made the first mass spectrograph, mostly with his own hands. He was well rewarded. Not only did the neon lines (no longer in this machine parabolae) show conclusively that the density of neon required isotopes to explain it (actually 3, that at 21 being weak) but he found that a great many other elements also had isotopes wholly unsuspected. This opened up a new world for the chemists. All true atomic weights became, very nearly, whole numbers; the apparent fractions, as in the case of neon, being due to the supposed element being composed of two or more isotopes of different mass. This pointed strongly back to an idea more than a century old and known as Prout's hypothesis which chemical science, after long hesitation, had decisively rejected a few decades before; namely that all elements were made of hydrogen. With the modification that neutrons as well as protons occur in nuclei this may be said to be the now accepted view.

But the rewards for Aston's faith and skill did not stop here. He soon found that though very nearly integers on a certain scale the weight of the atoms showed small variations. Hydrogen in particular was definitely over unity. This was immediately explicable on Einstein's law of the equivalence of mass and energy. If atoms of hydrogen, or rather the protons they contain, join to form the nuclei of heavier atoms there must be forces to hold them together and energy would be needed to separate them. This energy implies extra mass in the protons which must be heavier when separated than when combined. The loss of mass will depend on the force with which they are bound together. If one takes a proton in a nucleus of oxygen as an arbitrary standard a free proton will be heavier, while a proton in some other nucleus may be heavier or lighter according to how it is bound. Further, by measuring these small 'packing fractions' as Aston called them one can determine at once whether a hypothetical nuclear reaction would release or absorb energy. Before nuclear energy became a practical proposition Aston's work was there to show how much energy was available if ever it could be released.

Aston was a lifelong bachelor, precise in habits just as he was meticulously exact in laboratory work. He had perhaps a little of the old maid in his make-up, but he was a competent climber and more than competent skier, skater, and swimmer. The fingers which were so skilful in glass-blowing handled a tennis racket and a golf club with over average ability. He was fond of travel, especially by ship and took part in the observations of several eclipses. He had a taste for music and painting and in later life collected oriental china. His opinions on matters outside physics were conventional but were held with a charming diffidence. He was perfectly aware that some of his many friends thought his views behind the times but he was also aware, so at least I believe and hope, that they all regarded him with affection and that genuine respect which is compatible with occasional amusement. As an experimentalist he has seldom been equalled and probably never surpassed. He petted an apparatus as a musician might a violin, and if it failed to respond he was miserable.

ROBERT A. MILLIKAN

ROBERT A. MILLIKAN was one of the foremost active physicists in the United States for most of the first half of this century. He was the son of a preacher and brought up under pioneer, or near-pioneer, conditions in small towns in Illinois and Iowa. When he was born in 1872 American physics had indeed its great men: Willard Gibbs, the unrecognized genius, Michelson of the famous experiment, Rowland, whose ruling of accurate diffraction gratings made modern spectroscopy possible, were all active. But there was no second eleven. Only at a few universities were physics seriously studied, even when Millikan left school. The Physical Society had then only just been founded and the *Physical Review*, now the greatest journal of physics in the world, had yet to appear. In physics, as in most other sciences, the United States was in quantity, if not in quality, far behind several European nations. By his death in 1953 it had the greatest output of valuable work of any. Millikan had a substantial share in bringing this change about, both by his own work and by his influence on teaching and on government action.

Though he did much else, his best known work is that on the electron and after it that on the photoelectric effect. In the latter he was inspired by Einstein's belief that light travels in quanta, as photons, and that when a photon is absorbed it can give all its energy to one electron. When Einstein put this view forward in 1905 (*see* p. 118) the experimental evidence was not very strong. The photoelectric effect, in which light, usually ultraviolet, ejects electrons from certain solids such as zinc, though long known was notoriously capricious. This is because the ejection depends critically on the electrical state of the surface, expressed as the work required to pull an electron out. This in turn depends on the cleanness of the surface. In many cases a single layer of atoms is enough to make a large difference. Even in the best vacua obtainable such cleanliness was, and indeed still is, hard to achieve and retain. Millikan prepared his surfaces by shaving them in the vacuum in which they were to be used, using a tool moved by magnets outside the evacuated vessel—a vacuum barber's shop he called it. Even so the surfaces were not completely clean, but their contamination was at least constant during the experiment and this was all that was needed to establish that the energy given to an electron by the light was $h\nu$: Planck's constant multiplied by the frequency of the light. This put Einstein's belief on a firm experimental foundation.

When Millikan started his work on the charge of electrons in 1906 the value of the charge was uncertain by at least 50 per cent. Furthermore all the methods measured an *average* over many electrons. There was no real proof that all electrons have the same charge, or in other words that a natural unit of charge really exists. True, there was a strong presumption; electrolytic charges on ions when not the same are accurately twice or thrice the minimum, also when cathode rays are bent by a magnet those with the same velocity all deflect equally to a much greater accuracy than the measurement of e. But this deflection can be shown to depend on the *ratio* of charge to mass. As far as this experiment goes electrons might have different charges if they had proportionately differing masses. It did not seem very likely, but was certainly possible. Millikan adapted and improved a method previously used by H. A. Wilson, depending on the motion of charged drops of water driven by an electric force. He used drops of oil which did not evaporate during the experiment and by other improvements in technique produced one of the most beautiful experiments in physics. A tiny drop of oil is watched in a microscope while it falls slowly through the air. Then the air is ionized by X-rays and in time the drop will pick up one of the ions and get a charge; perhaps positive, perhaps negative. If gravity alone is acting this produces no appreciable effect, but if a vertical electric field is applied the drop will immediately accelerate or slow up according to whether the electric force acting on the charge on the drop pulls it down or up. This in turn depends on the sign of the charge (+ or —) and the direction of the electric intensity in the applied field. Millikan found that he could follow a particle in the microscope for hours at a time, letting it fall under gravity with the field off and then pulling it back by switching the field on, playing cup and ball with it so to speak. From these two speeds with a knowledge of the field and of the resistance of the air one can calculate the charge.

The charges were not always the same and sometimes changed suddenly, but however they changed *they were always exact multiples of a certain unit.* This is direct proof of a unit charge. The actual value was substantially more than that found before for the ions produced by X-rays, though not far from that deduced by Rutherford from experiments on alpha rays. It differed little from that used today.

Millikan was an excellent teacher and writer of textbooks, which were badly needed in America when he was a young man. Indeed he made a considerable reputation in this way before he was known for his research. He started as a teacher before he had taken a course. The Professor of Greek at the small mid-west college of Oberlin where he was, told him at the end of one year to teach elementary physics next session and overruled the objection that he did not know any! As was the custom at this period in America, Millikan later went to Germany, then the leading scientific country, where he attended Planck's lectures and worked under Nernst. It was an exciting period, for during it Röntgen discovered X-rays. Millikan was much influenced by his stay in Germany. He formed friendships, but was deeply shocked by the militaristic attitude of many of those whom he met. Later when war came he was among the first to urge that the United States should prepare to do her part in it. He supported George Hale, the astronomer, in setting up the National Research Council for this purpose, of which Hale was made President. It was an offshoot of what was then a decidedly elderly National Academy, founded for a rather similar reason in the Civil War. Even before the United States came into the war he sacrificed his promising research at Chicago for full-time work in Washington, where I later had the privilege of serving under him. Millikan was made a Vice-Chairman and Director of Research and Executive Officer of the Council, and started to work on anti-submarine devices. Later on his responsibility covered a much wider field and he was put into army uniform somewhat against his will. No one could have been less like the traditional soldier, but he got on well with them in spite of (or perhaps because of) occasional explosions. He showed great common sense at a time when this was the rarest, as well as the most needed, quality.

Shortly after the war he went to the California Institute of Technology, then a young and struggling foundation, and turned it into one of the great Colleges of the world. His influence in the world of education was exerted in favour of combining research and teaching, even at undergraduate level, and it is largely due to him that the Universities in the United States have retained the dominant position in the research of the country which they still hold. The United States is unique in the extent to which research, paid for by government, is conducted under the influence of Universities even when not actually on the campus.

Millikan retained all his life much of the pioneer simplicity of his immediate ancestors. He had profound and simple beliefs on questions of right and wrong and clung to them firmly. His passionate devotion to peace did not hinder him from helping in two wars when he felt that moral issues were at stake. He was completely lacking in affectation and pomposity; one might not agree with what he said but his reasons were perfectly clear. He was charming with young men. Some complained that he was too ready to boost work with which he had been in some way concerned, but the work was at least worth boosting.

IV

WHAT ARE THINGS MADE OF?

II. NUCLEI

RUTHERFORD'S discovery of the nucleus was an unexpected consequence of a long and very fruitful series of experiments on radioactivity. The actual discovery of radioactivity is due to the French physicist Becquerel. As is well known Pierre and Marie Curie improved on it by isolating first polonium and then radium, but a few lines may be given to Becquerel's discovery.

As a direct consequence of Röntgen's discovery of X-rays physicists in many countries looked for other possible radiations, and especially fluorescence, since the production of X-rays was supposed erroneously to be connected with the fluorescence of the glass of the bulb caused by the cathode rays. Some compounds of uranium are fluorescent, that is when illuminated by light of certain colours they produce light of characteristic colour different from that of the original light. Becquerel thought it worth trying what uranium compounds might do in the dark, and found that they could blacken photographic plates near them even if covered with black paper. Becquerel deserves credit for his enterprise, but he was lucky that it led to such a tremendous discovery. Radioactivity is not in fact connected with fluorescence, which is limited to some only of the compounds of uranium while radioactivity is an atomic property common to all bodies containing uranium.

Rutherford studied the three types of rays which the various radioactive substances produced and which he called alpha, beta and gamma in the order of their penetrating power. In the course of a long series of brilliant experiments he showed that radioactive atoms are unstable, that they change spontaneously, evolving energetic radiations in the process and producing other atoms which are usually radioactive in their turn, till at the end of a long chain of such processes a normal inert atom, usually of lead, is produced. He proved that the alpha rays are atomic bullets shot off in the course of this process and identical with atoms of the known gas helium, except that they lack the two electrons which a normal helium atom contains. However, before they come to rest they pick these up from the surrounding matter. This was of course a most startling discovery. These supposedly eternal atoms not only decayed but some of the bits were lighter atoms of a completely different kind from the originals. The beta rays turned out to be fast electrons, and the gamma rays to be a kind of X-ray.

Rutherford had a particular affection for alpha rays. He found that it was possible to detect a single individual, and thus count atoms. One way of doing this was to use a screen covered with small crystals of zinc sulphide. This fluoresces under the radiation as had long been known. If the source is weak, the observer's eye suitably rested by a long wait in the dark, and if a low-power microscope is used, it is possible to see individual flashes in the field of view of the microscope, and with practice to count them. Rutherford and his pupils used this method to study what happened when alpha rays went through matter, and Geiger found not unexpectedly that in going through thin gold foils they are scattered through small angles, presumably as a result of collision with the atoms they pass. However, using plates of solid metal Geiger and Marsden had found that a few are bent so much that they come out from the same side as that on which they entered. Even with a foil only ·004 cm. thick one in 20,000 was scattered through more than a right-angle, though in a foil of this thickness the mean angle of scattering was less than a degree.

At first sight it does not seem very surprising that a few rays should be turned through angles much greater than the average and many lesser men would have considered them unimportant. But to Rutherford, who insisted on forming a physical picture of what happened in his experiments, they were astonishing. 'It was quite the most incredible event that has ever happened to me in my life. It was almost as incredible as if you had fired a 15-inch shell at a piece of tissue paper and it had come back and hit you.'

So he spoke of it afterwards. If such a comparison seems far-fetched one must remember that for a single atom to be able to produce, quite unaided by any amplification, an effect large enough for the eye to detect is something remarkable and Rutherford was impressed with the energy and vigour of his alpha particles.

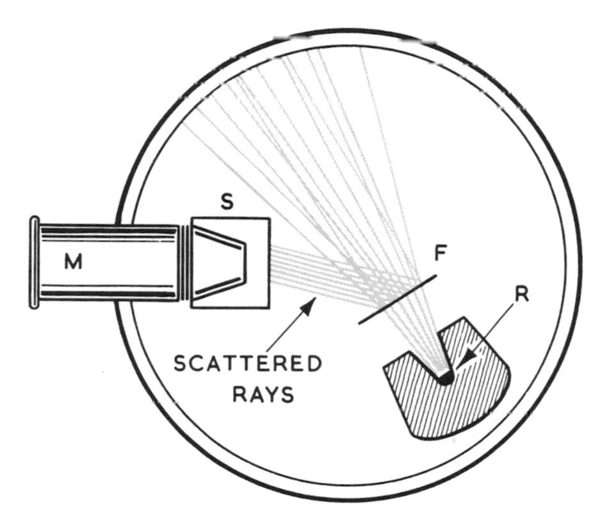

FIG. 6. GEIGER AND MARSDEN. SCATTERING OF ALPHA RAYS

The box, shown with its lid removed, turns on an air-tight joint carrying the microscope *M*, and the screens, round the foil *F*, which is irradiated by the source *R*.

For clarity the only scattered rays shown are those that hit the screen *S*.

He first satisfied himself that these 90° deflections were not merely the results of chance by which one particle had happened to acquire a number of small deflections all in the same direction. This must indeed *very* occasionally occur, but one can calculate from the extent of the small angle scattering how often it will happen and it does so vastly less often than is observed. The two effects are essentially separate and the large angle scattering is due to something that happens to each alpha particle only once if at all.

It is immediately obvious that it cannot be a collision with an electron, for the alpha particle is thousands of times more massive. If one thinks of a billiard ball colliding with a ping-pong ball at rest it is obvious that the former's track could never be turned through more than a very small angle. An alpha particle is four times as massive as a proton, so even a proton could not turn it through a right-angle. To turn it through more than a right-angle the particle struck must be more massive than the alpha. There must be some part of an atom of gold which is considerably heavier than an alpha particle and cemented together sufficiently firmly to act as a single body under the great shock of impact. Rutherford guessed that this body might account both for the main mass of the atom and supply the positive electric charge needed to neutralize the negative charge of the electrons. Alpha rays, as he had shown long before, have themselves a positive charge. They would be repelled by the hypothetical body, and sweep past it in a curve. The problem is closely similar to a comet coming in from outer space and sweeping past the sun, except that in this case the force is attractive. The change of sign makes little difference to the mathematics. In both cases the curve is an hyperbola, in both cases the more directly the moving object is aimed at the fixed one, provided it does not actually hit, the larger the angle through which its path will be turned. On the whole, well-directed shots will be rare and so will large angles of scattering. Rutherford worked out the pattern of scattering, the pattern, that is, of the alpha rays on the scintillating screen, that one should expect assuming one massive scattering centre per atom. The result depends of course on how large a positive charge is assumed, i.e. on how many electrons there are needing to be neutralized in an atom of gold, or of the other metals used. The bigger the charge the more spread out would the pattern be.

When the calculations were compared with experiments made by Geiger for the purpose the patterns agreed well, taking in the case of gold a charge sufficient to neutralize about 100 electrons.

It was a couple of years before the full importance of these results was realized. Then two other pieces of work, both from Rutherford's laboratory in Manchester, came along. The first was a piece of theory by the young Danish physicist, Niels Bohr, who used the idea of a central charged nucleus to set out a revolutionary theory of the hydrogen atom and in particular how it produced light, using Planck's still hardly accepted quantum theory. The jubilee of the nucleus is being celebrated this year, 1961.

Next Moseley, killed a few years later in Gallipoli, applying and generalizing this theory to include other atoms and the X-rays characteristic of them, showed that it all fitted in with Rutherford's idea if one supposed that the number of unit charges on what was now beginning to be called the nucleus was equal to the place of the atom in the accepted list of chemical elements. With a few irregularities this was the same as the list in order of increasing atomic weight. The name 'atomic number' was introduced for the place in this order with hydrogen as one, helium as two, lithium as three and so on with increasing weights of the atoms. Moseley's experiments show a step-by-step change in certain properties of the secondary X-rays which are excited in a series of the heavier elements by subjecting them to primary X-rays. If the elements are in order of increasing atomic weight, each change from one to the next changes the properties of the X-rays produced by a definite and equal step. This is very clear evidence that the difference between one element and the next implies the change in some important property by a unit. Moseley's application of Bohr's theory to the production of secondary X-rays required that this property be the charge on the nucleus. So the conclusion is reached that the number of unit charges on the nucleus is identical with the atomic number defined as the order in the list of elements.* The atomic number for gold is 79 and this was within the rather wide range of error of Geiger's experiments. Later more accurate experiments of the same general kind have confirmed the agreement for gold and several other elements to within a unit. Since atoms in the ordinary state are neutral the atomic number of an element is also the number of electrons the atom contains in the normal state. The study of how these electrons behave and the very curious laws that govern

* At the time there were gaps in the series whose existence could be guessed from chemical evidence and which were confirmed by Moseley.

them took up a large part of the attention of physicists in the period between the wars, but I shall not discuss it further here.

It is however worth while noticing a little more carefully how Rutherford's discovery came about. There was first the clear conception he had formed of the alpha particle as a very forceful projectile which would take a lot to turn it. Then the discovery by Geiger and Marsden that some of them could be turned through a right-angle or more by a sheet of metal. Then the investigation of the small angle scattering. This was necessary to make sure that the large deflections, after all decidedly rare, were not the result of the superposition of a number of the understandable small collisions. This possibility of 'multiple scattering', not well understood at the time, is a complication always coming up in problems of scattering and one on which, as Rutherford showed in the paper quoted, earlier workers had gone astray. It is often quite a tricky mathematical problem. In this case once faced it was not very serious, multiple scattering is nowhere near being a factor of importance. Having decided that the experiments must be taken at their face value as showing the possibility of single large collisions, he then had to explain how these could occur. Here he was on safe grounds for Newtonian mechanics were undoubted (nowadays he might have been less sure!) It follows clearly from simple mechanical principles that there must be a centre in the atom more massive than the alpha and probably a great deal more so. Assuming only one, containing the main weight of the atom and having a positive charge, the mathematical calculation of the scattering is not too difficult. It would have been quite a fair problem to set in the Cambridge Mathematical Tripos. The genius of Rutherford lay in seeing the significance of an apparently rather ordinary experimental result, but this result came from the improvement in technique which by making it possible to count individual alphas enabled Geiger and Marsden to detect the very few particles turned back.

Later it was to be shown, mostly by Rutherford and his pupils, that the nucleus is a complex body composed of protons and a new entity called a neutron. This is a particle slightly heavier than a proton but with no charge. In both these matters the neutron resembles a hydrogen atom but its diameter, in so far as it can be said to have one, is something like a hundred thousand times smaller. Consequently, it passes through solid matter with relatively little resistance. All nuclei are small compared with their atoms. Most of the space in the atom is occupied by the electrons 'like a swarm of gnats in a cathedral' it has been said, but perhaps they are better pictured as thin floating clouds. The term 'nucleon' has been introduced with the meaning of proton or neutron. These particles are held together against the mutual electrical repulsion of the protons by a force of a special kind whose precise nature is still a mystery, called simply the nuclear force. Sufficiently violent impacts from other nuclei can break up nuclei often in several alternative ways. Neutrons can be knocked out of nuclei in various ways, for example by alpha rays bombarding berylium. Because of the repulsion of the like charges nuclei can only get to grips with one another if they move with considerable energy, but to this rule isolated neutrons are an exception. Since neutrons are uncharged they can approach nuclei closely even when moving slowly and often coalesce with them. Since the resulting complex has the same positive charge, and hence the same atomic number as the original atom, it is an isotope of it. However, it sometimes happens that this complex nucleus is unstable and breaks up into two or more parts. The production of nuclear energy from uranium, both explosively and in reactors for the generation of power, requires processes of this kind.

ERNEST RUTHERFORD

It is very seldom that one man, however great, creates a whole branch of science. Yet it is only a moderate exaggeration to say that Rutherford created nuclear physics, including the earlier study of radioactivity which it has now absorbed. It is true that Becquerel made the first discovery and the Curies showed that the effect in uranium, as it occurs naturally, is due to a variety of elements and isolated two of them, namely polonium and radium. Then Crookes extracted a radioactive component whose activity decays exponentially in a matter of days, while the activity of the remaining uranium increases so that the two together produce a constant effect. Of the rest, from the time he went to Montreal in 1898 till he died in 1937, the lion's share of the most important work was done by himself and the co-workers and pupils whom he inspired and taught.

Together with Soddy he proved that radioactive atoms are not permanent but spontaneously change into others, and later he showed that in many cases they make atoms of helium, an accepted non-radioactive element. This was not the first occasion on which the supposed immunity of atoms from change had been broken, since J.J. had shown that electrons could be torn off atoms by X-rays to leave an 'ion' with a positive charge. Indeed, Rutherford, then recently arrived from New Zealand with a grant provided by the 1851 Commissioners, had helped J.J. in some of these experiments. But the ions if left alone rapidly recombined, thus restoring the broken atoms. Rutherford's breaks were far more drastic, and quite permanent. A radioactive atom could become two, one usually also radioactive, the other an atom of helium, or more strictly the fast-moving ion of helium, which he had named an alpha particle and which by picking up two electrons became a helium atom. In other cases there is an emission of an electron which, because it comes from the nucleus, changes the nuclear charge and therefore the chemical nature of the atom.

Twenty years after he left Cambridge he returned to it as J.J.'s successor, where he was to develop a discovery made in Manchester into a systematic examination of the transformations the alphas could cause in the lighter elements, the atoms of which he proved to be breakable. In this he used alphas as natural projectiles to transform elements, but when in 1933 Cockcroft and Walton, working in the Cavendish under Rutherford, produced disintegration by atomic projectiles accelerated by the methods of electrical engineering, the human control of atoms seemed complete. It was not quite so. Nuclear fission, which is the division of the nuclei of uranium or a few other heavy elements into two roughly equal parts with an energy release much exceeding that of natural radioactivity, did not come till after Rutherford's death and was discovered on the Continent. But even here he had a share. The neutrons, which produced the fission, had been discovered before his death by Chadwick in the Cavendish after several attempts which he had inspired. Hahn, who if he did not make quite the final discovery certainly opened the way to it, was an old pupil of the Montreal days.

Nuclear fission, of course, led straight to the power-producing reactor and to the 'atomic' bomb. These he neither saw nor foresaw. He repeatedly and strongly maintained till his death that the nucleus he had discovered was unlikely ever to have any large-scale practical application. When I recall his words I find it hard to believe that physicists are much to blame for failing to foresee the consequences of scientific discoveries yet to be made.

Rutherford was a moderate mathematician, and Townsend and he were the two first 'research students' at the Cavendish under J.J. when that status was first officially established. Townsend, an Irishman of wit and charm who afterwards became Professor at Oxford, was a good mathematician and people used to say that though of course both were very good Townsend would go farther because of this. Incidentally, a story of those days is worth telling, though it is less characteristic of Rutherford than of Townsend. A distinguished French physicist was staying with J.J. and Mrs. Thomson, and the two research students were asked to dinner to meet him. The Frenchman knew no language but his own, and was not very familiar with the world outside France, for when he was told that Rutherford came from New Zealand he rolled his eyes up in some horror and said that he thought people from that country were dark and did not they eat one another? Townsend could talk French well, but Rutherford could only understand without power of replying, as Townsend explained that New Zealanders pretended nowadays that they had given up these practises—but of course!

Rutherford's genius lay in his uncanny physical insight, combined with a flair for designing very simple experiments which worked. In both these he showed what is fundamentally the same quality, namely the ability to see the essential and discard all the rest. He would have been an outstanding success in any walk of life, except perhaps the artistic, but his physical insight was a special gift. Atoms and alpha particles were as real to him as his friends.

He was a big man physically, and looked somehow bigger than he was. In appearance he was like a prosperous farmer, not unnaturally since he had been brought up on a farm. He was bluff in manner, forthright in what he said, a man of immense energy. He often spoke, not entirely in joke, of the need to keep theorists in their place in physics, but had a great regard for Niels Bohr who had been with him for a time at Manchester. Chemistry he regarded as the next best thing to physics, but a long way behind. He was a great leader of his 'boys', and they loved him for his human qualities quite as much as for his scientific ones. Somehow, while very active in affairs he managed to find time for teaching as well as research. His lectures were excellent and his informal talks almost better. He was fully aware of the importance of what he was doing (how could he fail to be?) and great enough to admit it. On the occasion of one of his discoveries a friend said, 'You are a lucky man, Rutherford, always on the crest of the wave!' 'Well! I made the wave, didn't I?—at least to some extent.' He had faith in physics as something immensely worth doing, and no doubts.

Perhaps his one great sorrow was the early death of his only daughter. One of his grandsons is a physicist.

V

THE POINT OF VIEW—CONCEPTS OF SPACE AND TIME

THE idea of up-and-down is intuitive; we have indeed a special organ, the semicircular canals, whose business it is to tell us which way is 'up', and when it goes wrong we feel giddy. For greater accuracy the plumb line was invented. It seemed clear that all plumb lines point the same way and the existence of a common vertical direction must have helped to create the concept of parallel lines. When the idea was put forward that the earth is spherical, one of the objections was that people on the other side would fall off. Greek philosophy was divided. The Atomists, followers of Democritus and Epicurus who were in most ways nearest to a scientific outlook, were in this case unperceptive. They clung to a flat earth and maintained that all the atoms fell 'downwards' in the void. By a queer perversity this rather stupid error led to a brilliant suggestion that can be read by the very imaginative as a precognition of the 'indeterminacy' now associated with the quantum theory—but this is a digression. Other Greeks accepted a spherical earth with the implication that the plumb line is not everywhere parallel. In fact Eratosthenes made a remarkably good measurement of the earth's radius by measuring the angle between the sun at noon on midsummer day and the vertical at two places approximately North and South along the Nile.* He must have realized that up-and-down is not an absolute direction and that the plumb bob tries to seek the centre of the earth, but it took Newton to explain this as a consequence of an attraction exerted on the bob by every particle of the earth. This extension of the idea of up-and-down to suit a spherical earth is one of the earliest examples of the generalization of a concept. It is a considerable feat of imagination to realize that a

* It is not certain how long his 'stade' was. If it was ten to a modern mile he was practically dead right.

direction which is up-and-down to one man may perhaps be horizontal to another. It was only the first of many such exercises which science demands of man.

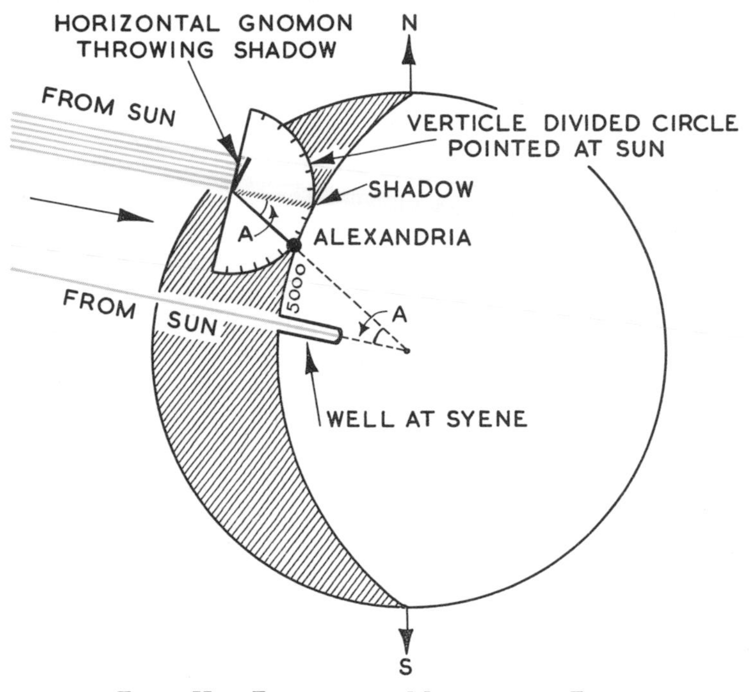

FIG. 7. HOW ERATOSTHENES MEASURED THE EARTH

At midsummer the sun at midday shone to the bottom of a deep well at Syene far up the Nile. At the same time he measured its angle *A* to a plumb line at Alexandria, probably by using a shadow as drawn. Alexandria was believed to be 5,000 stades north of Syene.

A is also the angle between the radii of the earth that go through Syene and Alexandria respectively. The radius of the earth bears the same ratio to 5,000 stades that the radius of the divided circle does to the arc between the plumb line and the shadow.

The next upset of commonsense ideas came from astronomy and concerned relative motion, in this case angular motion or spin. It is obvious to any observer that the stars as a whole swing ound on an axis roughly through the Pole Star about once a day. f one once accepts a spherical earth it is almost equally obvious hat the same appearance would be achieved by the earth's spin- ing and the stars standing still. As we shall see later on there are experiments which can be made on earth that at least appear to distinguish between these two views, but they were not known when the issue was disputed. Even when one has made one's choice in the matter of the stars there is a further pair of alterna- tives for the sun. The sun rises and sets each day at a slightly different place against the background of such stars as can be seen near it, retreating gradually through the sky. This is equivalent to saying that the line joining earth and sun, or more precisely their centres, rotates slowly (in fact once round in a year) with respect to the stars. In this case also one can choose which is unmoved, sun or earth. These two pairs of alternatives can be combined giving four possibilities, but in practice two have been the more important; namely earth at rest and unspinning so that both sun and stars go round it though at slightly different rates, and the Copernican view that the stars and sun are still, while the earth rotates once a day,* and so goes round the sun once a year. However, Hicetas of Syracuse and Heracleides of Pontus (*b.* about 388 B.C.) believed the stars to be at rest and the earth spinning, but remaining at the centre of the system with the sun going round it.

Greek astronomy spent much effort on the problem, which is much complicated, though not altered in essentials, by the need of accounting for the motions of the moon and planets. Several solu- tions were put forward based on the hypothesis of a central fixed earth. They all needed a number of spheres, usually thirty or more, which were supposed to 'carry' the sun, moon and planets, besides one for the stars. It is not quite clear how far these invisible spheres were regarded as having real existence, like the jelly of a nineteenth-century ether, and how far they were just a mathe- matical mode of description, as a more modern ether might be. Probably different writers felt differently. These theories were

* Strictly speaking, this is a sidereal day, which differs from the ordinary mean solar day by about 1 part in 365¼.

very valuable because they were quantitative and made to fit observed facts, 'to save the phenomena' as the phrase went, a most important idea that here for the first time comes into science fully and clearly. One set of theories, due originally to Eudoxus and extended by Aristotle, had all its spheres concentric with the earth but with their axes set at various angles and spinning in imaginary bearings carried by other spheres. Another set of theories, which was on the whole more popular in the Middle Ages, though rather doubtfully better, was due to Ptolemy. It used epicycles, i.e. movements like those of spheres rolling inside or outside other spheres, the latter were supposed to have the earth as centre.

Though Aristarchos of Samos had suggested in about 250 B.C. an arrangement with the sun at the centre, this had been forgotten and when Copernicus put forward his famous theory he was making an original discovery. Copernicus's book, published in 1543 just before his death, inspired Galileo and in the end won the struggle against the traditional belief. It was a change of view-point that affected men's thoughts very deeply by making the earth subordinate to the sun and stars. It also led through Kepler, the astronomer, to Newton's theory of gravitation. Instead of the great complication of spheres the planets now were seen to move each in a well-known curve, an ellipse with its focus at the sun, and the motion obeyed two other simple laws. It became a starting point for further progress as the ideas of Ptolemy or Eudoxus could never have done, though with enough spheres one could have 'saved the phenomena' to any accuracy one cared. It is not enough, though necessary, for a theory to account for the facts, it must use good concepts. Those of an orbit and of forces acting to a centre not only made the mathematics simpler, but what is even more important could be applied to other things. As Newton saw on that famous occasion, the moon and a falling apple are examples of the same effect.

We see in this development the beginning of an understanding of relative motion, in this case relative spin, an idea which came in so to speak by the back door. We have not finished with the idea of relative spin, but before going on with it, it is desirable to say something of a simpler type of relative motion, namely motion in a straight line. To study it one needs to consider the ideas of space and time more closely.

A physicist nowadays thinks of space as a collection of relations of a special kind between objects. These relations require as a rule the measurement of distances and angles, or at least their estimation which is just a name for inaccurate measurement. Some relations however are qualitative, for example the difference between the inside and the outside of the (unbroken) skin of an orange, which remains essentially the same however the skin is squeezed or distorted provided only it is not torn.

It is worth noticing that measurements are only possible if one has available approximately rigid bodies for measuring rods, stiff enough to stay nearly straight. They need not be precisely rigid. The surveyor can, and does, allow for changes in the size of his rods or tapes due to expansion by heat or by strain but he can only measure these changes against a background that can be assumed to be very nearly unchanged in dimensions. Even if one tries to use rays of light as natural straight lines, which might be allowable on an astronomical scale, they would be useless to measure angles of sight without some sort of rigid sextant or theodolite.

Newton believed in absolute space, so that a body might be absolutely at rest. However, the laws he found for mechanics are such that uniform absolute motion is undetectable. A set of bodies will behave in just the same way, according to Newton, whatever their absolute velocity in a straight line provided their relative velocities are the same. He also believed in absolute time. Here he seems to have been concerned with the difficulty of being sure which of several clocks is right. For example, time measured by the apparent motion of the stars is different from that measured by the sun, not only because there is one more sidereal day than solar day in a year, but because the relation between the two varies slightly with the time of year. For theoretical reasons Newton took, correctly, the sidereal time as 'right', and though for convenience we use an approximately solar day it is fictitious and does not follow the real sun. This is why the mornings are so dark after Christmas, though the evenings are opening out. In Newton's time clocks were not very accurate, but it is possible now to show that good clocks whether they depend on pendulums, or on spring-controlled balance wheels, on oscillating quartz crystals or on molecular oscillations will agree together and with the apparent motion of the stars but not with that of the sun.

A 'clock' in fact is just a device for counting how often a particular process has occurred, the swing of a pendulum, the oscillation of a crystal or even the rotation of the earth. The process is assumed always to take the same time, and the justification is this possibility of finding many such processes which give concordant results.

But the phrase 'absolute time' can be used in a different sense. It may be taken to mean that time is the same for everyone and Newton probably thought so. In this sense however he was wrong. If people in widely different places are to compare time they must either use the same clock or set their clocks. People on the earth can use the same clock, namely the stars as seen from our rotating earth, and this is all they need for time *intervals*, to compare for example the performance of runners. But if they want to *synchronize* their clocks by use of the stars they need also to know the difference in longitude, for a star will be in the zenith in different longitudes at different times. For every degree change in longitude the time changes by four minutes. In former days high quality chronometers, if two agreed, were assumed not to have changed their rates by being transported across the sea, and by combination of their readings with an astronomical measurement the longitude was found—the argument thus being reversed. Now with cables and radio which carry signals with nearly the speed of light clocks can be synchronized directly, and incidentally the longitude determined with great accuracy. Theoretically one must take account of the time the signal takes, though it is less than 1/10 sec. over the earth. This is done by sending a signal back the moment one is received. Half the time between sending the first signal and receiving the return one back is taken as the time to go either way. This of course *assumes* that the times in the two directions are the same. As long as the two stations are at rest with respect to each other this is perfectly satisfactory.

If we are ever able to communicate with people in distant space we could get them to understand our units of time and of length by referring to atomic processes. For example, the radiation due to hydrogen of 21 cm. wavelength which is prominent in the radiation from space could be used to explain what a centimeter is, and the oscillation of one of the natural molecular clocks could give a unit of time.

The difficulties with time and space began to appear when Maxwell first succeeded in stating correctly the laws concerning the relations between electric and magnetic quantities. Incidentally, his theory first predicted the existence of the electromagnetic waves which Hertz later discovered experimentally and which are now called radio. It also implies that light is itself a form of electromagnetic waves, and predicts correctly that the velocity of light can be calculated from laboratory measurements of electricity and magnetism. Now Maxwell's equations, unlike Newton's, do imply absolute rest, in the sense that a set of bodies 'at rest' should behave differently from the same set in steady motion. For example, a charged electrical condenser with parallel plates should show a tendency to rotate if moving, but not if at rest. This quality of Maxwell's theory did not surprise or trouble anyone at first. The nineteenth-century physicists were used to ethers, and though Maxwell's ether was a curious one it was actually implicit in his theory. Now, of course, an ether supplies just the privileged frame of reference needed to assign a meaning to absolute rest. Anyone who raises philosophical objections to the idea of absolute rest can be answered 'this means at rest relative to the ether'.

Unfortunately experiments made in this way to detect the motion of the earth always failed. Now since the earth moves round the sun it cannot be at 'rest' at all times of year, even if at one particular date its motion round the sun is just cancelled by the (unknown) motion of the sun itself. However, its velocity in orbit is only about 1 in 10,000 of the velocity of light so all the experimenters can hope for is a small effect.

One way out is to reject Maxwell's theory and this perhaps might have been done, in spite of its great success, had it not been for the equal failure of Michelson's famous attempt to detect this same motion by optical means. In this experiment light from a source is divided into two beams by a slightly silvered mirror which will reflect part and transmit the rest. These two beams each go backwards and forwards over distances equal but in directions at right-angles, e.g. one east-west, the other north-south. They are then brought together and produce light and dark bands called 'interference fringes'. Assuming light to be a wave-motion the position of the fringes in effect measures the *difference* in the times the two beams have taken to travel over their equal but differently directed paths. If the apparatus really is moving through an ether a simple calculation shows that the total time for a path up and down stream is slightly more than for an equal distance across stream and back. The direction of motion, if any, is unknown, but the apparatus can be rotated so that the path which in one setting takes the longer time should in another setting take the shorter. No significant shift of the fringes was observed. Michelson's experiment is based on a very general argument about waves which is valid for almost any kind of waves in almost any sort of ether, including Maxwell's electromagnetic waves. Altering Maxwell's theory a bit, or even exchanging it for one of the many other forms of wave theory which had been suggested would not remove the difficulty. Another way out of the difficulty would be to suppose that the ether is carried along by the earth in its motion, but it is impossible to fit this view in with the well established 'aberration of light'. Each star appears to describe a tiny orbit in the sky once a year, of just the size it ought to have because of the relative motion of the earth and the light from the star, if the earth were moving through the ether. If the earth carries the ether the explanation cannot be made to work, without tearing the ether at the boundary.

The Michelson-Morley experiment was made in 1887. In 1892 the Irish physicist Fitzgerald, and almost simultaneously the great Dutch physicist Lorentz, put forward an ingenious idea to reconcile the facts with the idea of an ether. They supposed that any body, however rigid, moving through the ether contracts in the direction of motion by a certain fraction of its length while its sideways dimensions remain unchanged.

For ordinary speeds which are very small compared with the velocity of light the contraction is minute, but small or large it

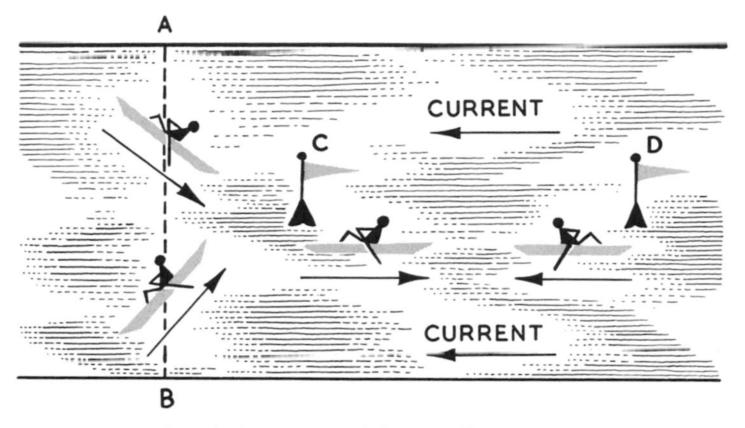

FIG. 8. MICHELSON-MORLEY EXPERIMENT

Here *AB* is equal to *CD*. The man rowing backwards and forwards from *A* to *B* *across* the stream has to point upstream to allow for the current sweeping him down; but even so has a slight advantage over the man who rows straight up stream *C* to *D* and then straight down stream back to *C*. In the actual experiment a beam of light is divided into two parts, one goes upstream, is reflected, and returns downstream, the other across-stream for an equal distance and is also reflected. The two are then brought together and produce a pattern of light and dark fringes which indicate the difference in time which the two beams have taken on their journeys.

could never be detected by ordinary measurement since the measuring rod would contract in the same proportion. The contraction exactly explains the absence of any effect in the Michelson-Morley experiment. At this time it was just beginning to be realized that the forces which hold ordinary matter together are electromagnetic in nature, so it was not unreasonable that they should be affected by motion through the ether and, if they were, the dimensions of an object would alter. However, to account for all the experiments one must also assume that clocks moving through the ether go slow by the same fraction by which rigid bodies shorten. Again this is not hopelessly implausible, but the whole idea was getting artificial. There seemed to be a conspiracy on the part of the laws of Nature to prevent motion through the ether ever being observed. Alice's White Knight had a scheme

To dye one's whiskers green,
And always use so large a fan
That they could not be seen,

but it seemed undignified of Nature!

At last Poincaré, the French mathematical physicist, brother of a French Premier, and Lorentz, were led to a more radical view. It was Poincaré who first spoke of the 'Theory of Relativity', but Lorentz's theoretical development of Maxwell's theory was an essential aid. The new view accepts as something fundamental the impossibility of measuring motion through the ether, which is nearly the same as rejecting the ether. An almost equivalent statement is that the velocity of light is the same for all observers.* This, however, is a surprising statement. As a matter of commonsense one would have expected that whether light was a stream of particles as Newton thought, or waves as had been believed for the last century, it should seem faster to an observer moving towards the source than to one moving away from it.

It now becomes necessary to reconsider time and space and relative motion, and in particular the relation between the statements that will be made by observers moving with respect to one another as to the sizes of objects and the times of events. As a mathematical problem there is virtually only one possible solution if the velocity of light is to be the same for all. This solution (known as the 'Lorentz transformation') implies, among other things, the contraction of lengths and the slowing of clocks previously suggested as rather arbitrary hypotheses.

* Strictly speaking this is only true in the absence of acceleration, which, however, the original theory did not consider.

But now that there is no ether with its privileged observer, a length will seem shorter to *any* observer past whom it is moving than it does to someone at rest beside it, and a clock will go slow to *any*one past whom it is moving, regardless of the direction of motion. In addition absolute simultaneity goes, and with it an absolute time order. Two events we shall see, may be judged to be in one order by one observer and in the reverse order by someone moving past him, but only if they occur a considerable distance apart. Events which occur at the same place are in the same time order for all observers.

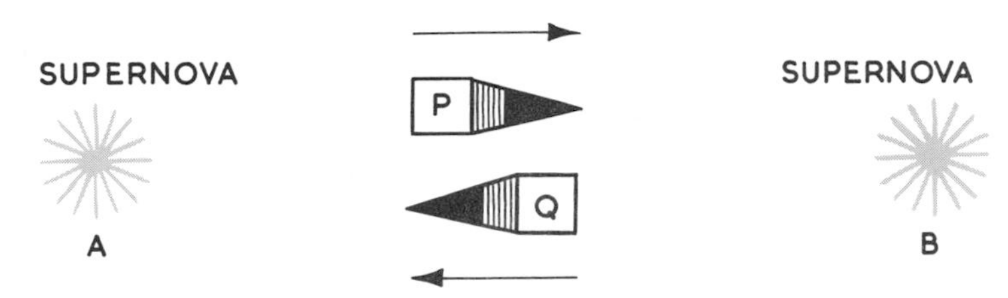

FIG. 9. The two observers *P* and *Q* are shown passing in space at the moment when each observes the birth of two supernovæ *A* and *B* which are at rest with respect to one another and the same distance from *P* and *Q*. *P* will conclude that *B* 'really' happened before *A* and *Q* that *A* 'really' happened before *B*.

The time of a distant event assigned by any observer includes allowance for the time light from the event takes to reach him. Suppose two observers near together but moving past one another observe the same event, say the birth of a supernova, in a direction which for simplicity we will take to be the same as that of the relative motion. Suppose they pass one another at the instant when they both see the new star, and know its distance. If one is moving from it and the other towards it with equal speeds* any contraction in distance or slowing of clocks will be the same for both, but one will conclude that the distance when the light was actually emitted was *more* than when he saw the light, the other that it was *less*. When each has made his correction using, as we

* The relative speed in line of sight of a star and an observer can be measured by changes in the light of the star when analysed in a spectroscope.

require him to do, a *constant* speed of light, the estimates of the times of emission are different, e.g. one might suppose it to have been 1,000 years ago, the other 1,100. (They would have been the same if each had added or subtracted his own speed from that of light before doing the calculation, but this is against the rule of constant velocity for light.) If another supernova had been also seen at the time the observers crossed at the same distance but in the opposite direction, the dates would have been reversed. Thus each would suppose the event (in this case the stellar explosion) towards which he was moving to have been 'really' the earlier. The actual seeing of the supernovae by the two observers are events which because they happen in the same place are truly simultaneous. This effect is apt to be larger than the contractions. In mathematical language it is a first order effect while they are second order. When the velocity reverses the first order effect changes its sign from plus to minus or minus to plus while the contraction is always a contraction, *each* of the two in relative motion judges the other shorter than it would have been at rest.

A very strong point in favour of this theory is that the same mathematical relations which make the velocity of light the same for all do the equivalent for Maxwell's equations which thus become equally valid for all observers. The Principle of Relativity asserts that fundamental physical laws have the same form for all observers who move past one another with uniform motion in a straight line. Thus Maxwell's equations now conform to this Principle. It should be noticed that this Principle is an assertion that the laws are *absolute*. The expression 'Principle of Relativity' is an example of the ambiguity which can come from a rather vague preposition, the analogy is to the 'Principles *of* War' rather than the 'Principle *of* Self-determination'. It tells you how to deal with relative motion; it does *not* say that this is particularly important or desirable, still less that all things are only relative.

Though this treatment gets over some difficulties, it does so at the cost of considerable violence to commonsense. It may be doubted if it would have received the full acceptance that it in fact has but for the remarkable applications to mechanics, largely due to Einstein, leading to predictions concerning the identity of mass and energy which have been brilliantly verified in nuclear physics, but we reserve these to a later chapter. 'Special' Relativity, as this form is called, is an example of how understanding physics depends on getting the right basic approach. Instead of dealing with the difficulties caused by unexpected and, to the theorist, disconcerting experimental results by patching up and plugging holes, Poincaré and Einstein took the drastic line of starting entirely afresh and discarding concepts such as an absolute time order for events which while perfectly satisfactory for ordinary life turn out to be inadequate when large velocities come in.

'Special' Relativity deals only with constant velocity in a straight line. What happens when the velocity changes either in magnitude or direction? Such a change in velocity is called acceleration, using this word as a general term, a decrease of velocity being considered a negative acceleration and a change in direction as an acceleration at right-angles to the velocity. It is the quantity round which the mechanics of Galileo and Newton was built. Forces are known by the accelerations they produce. For a particle this is equal in each case to the force divided by the mass.*

Among these forces is gravity. This force is unique in that it alone is always proportional (at any one place) to the *mass* of the body on which it acts. This means that at any one place the acceleration due to gravity is constant, or more briefly, all bodies fall equally fast from rest. Galileo first established this law in the famous experiment when he dropped a 1-lb. and 100-lb. weight together from the leaning tower of Pisa and showed that they arrived together (or nearly so) at the bottom, while the followers of Aristotle had held that their speeds should be proportional to their weights. Galileo's experiment was not very accurate, but experiments on pendulums—and the bob of a pendulum is really a gently falling body—have verified the law to one part in a million.

Because of this curious property of gravity people in a space-

* If more than one force acts the resulting accelerations add, taking account of their direction, or alternatively one can combine the forces according to a simple law to find a single 'resultant' i.e. effective force which can replace them.

ship cannot tell that they are 'falling' or which way gravity is acting, once they are out of the atmosphere. Even only 200 miles up where the earth's gravity is still ninety per cent. of the value at the surface, it is wholly inappreciable inside the ship because the ship itself and all that is in it is accelerating equally. No forces are required to keep objects together or to separate them slowly, and if two drift apart there is nothing to bring them together again. But if some other force is exerted, for example by firing a rocket, the acceleration of the case of the space-ship caused by the rocket will make loose objects inside it move to one of the walls in the direction of the rocket's burst as though they had suddenly acquired 'weight'.

Einstein's General Relativity is an attempt to generalize the 'Special' theory by admitting *any* kind of relative motion, but has been most successful as a theory of gravitation in competition with Newton's. It starts by taking as fundamental this remarkable constancy of acceleration at a given place. It postulates that a uniform gravitational field is indistinguishable from, indeed identical with, a state of uniform acceleration. Such a state of things cannot be detected by internal experiments, only by observation of something outside. Thus the quite substantial gravitational field of the sun which carries the earth round it once a year cannot be detected on earth, or rather could not if it were uniform. Because it is slightly greater on the side of the earth facing the sun than on the side turned from it tidal effects are caused which show up as the difference between spring and neap tides. Yet this detectable difference is 5,000 times less than the main effect of which we should be quite ignorant if we did not see the sun against the background of the stars and so infer the orbital motion of the earth.

The General Theory of Relativity however goes further than the equivalence of gravitation and acceleration. It asserts that *any* fundamental law, not only that of gravitation, must be expressible in a form which is the same for all observers, even those accelerated with respect to one another. This is really a mathematical statement, a restriction on the mathematical form such laws can have. It does *not* mean that all observers will observe the same effects.

For example, taking just Special Relativity which deals with velocities only, an observer moving past an electric charge will observe a magnetic force due to it, but one at rest with respect to it will not.

This mathematical problem for formulating laws which shall be in form equally valid for everyone is a difficult one, but Einstein solved it. It turns out, rather surprisingly, that there is one special law of this sort for gravitation so much simpler than any other, that it virtually selected itself. It is unfortunately difficult to apply and only a few simple cases have been worked out. When the gravity is weak the result becomes indistinguishable from Newton's law that any two particles attract with a force directly proportional to the product of their masses and inversely as the distance between them squared.

One is apt to consider gravity a strong force, but in fact it is very weak. Two spheres of lead each weighing a ton (on the earth) and with their centres a metre apart only attract with a force of about $\frac{1}{4000}$ of an ounce. Gravity is impressive to us because the earth, which does the attraction, is a very large body by ordinary standards.

Hence it is not surprising that for most purposes Newton and Einstein give the same result. Only three effects, all small, are known which can distinguish them, a peculiarity of the motion of the planet Mercury, the bending of light from a star that passes near the sun and a change in wavelength of light emitted in a gravitational field. In all three cases the experiments agree with Einstein's theory about as well as can be expected, but the effects are so small that the percentage errors are considerable and the agreement not very precise, except in the last case. Here recent experiments with X-rays, which are a form of light, have shown good agreement. Unfortunately this is the least decisive test of the three since the same result can be predicted merely by supposing that the energy of the X-rays is changed by the action of gravity as would be that of a bullet. Since all energy is the same in essence it would be surprising if it were not.

Few doubt that Einstein's theory is superior to Newton's in accuracy, though very much harder to use. Indeed, Newton's theory conflicts with Special Relativity. Newton's theory can only be strictly true for a specially privileged observer. If for example it were true of an observer at rest with respect to the sun, the theory could not then be strictly true for one on the earth. But General Relativity has not quite the compelling attraction of the Special Theory. It is not needed to explain a series of nul experiments as is the latter. In fact, absolute acceleration in the form of spin is detectable. One can prove that the earth is spinning and measure the length of a (sidereal) day by indoor experiments without seeing sun or star. If a pendulum is hung from a pivot which allows free rotation and set swinging, the plane of its motion will appear to change, simply because the earth is turning underneath it. This Foucault pendulum, though a century old, is not an accurate device; it is difficult to get a support which will not drag the pendulum round. However, the gyrocompass, now standard on board ship, though a much more complicated device and harder to understand, does essentially depend on the same basic principle. This is capable of a high degree of accuracy and behaves as Newton's theory demands. It is therefore possible to measure two 'days', one the time for the earth to rotate with respect to the visible stars and another purely mechanical, measured by Foucault's pendulum or its equivalent. These two agree, a remarkable fact. In this sense the stars constitute a frame of reference which has special properties and with respect to which the laws of dynamics take a particularly simple form.* A frame of reference with respect to which Newton's laws hold in the simplest form is technically called an 'inertial frame'. Thus lines of sight to the fixed stars form an inertial frame, but the lines of latitude and longitude on the earth do not. The Foucault pendulum swings in a plane in the inertial frame of the fixed stars.

It was suggested long ago in the nineteenth century by the Austrian physicist Mach (after whom the 'Mach number' in aeronautics is named) that the masses of the stars in some way created inertia and so formed a privileged system. Einstein agreed

* Any frame moving with uniform velocity with respect to them, and not turning, would do as well. This, of course, follows from Special Relativity.

with Mach that if all matter were destroyed except a test particle this would have no mass, i.e. no inertia.

Einstein's theory implies that space near a gravitating body is slightly non-Euclidian, that the theorem of Pythagoras is not strictly true. It has long been known that this theorem is not a logical necessity, but an experimental fact, at least to a high degree of accuracy. Planets move in the equivalent of straight lines in non-Euclidian space, lines which are interpreted by us as curves, in rather the same way that the shortest path between two places on the earth is a great circle not a straight line. Whittaker uses as a simile a game of bowls played in the North of England, in which the jack is on top of a slight mound. A bowl (without bias) approaching obliquely will turn away as though repelled by the jack. One could describe its motion by supposing the green flat and a suitable repulsion force acting. This is like what Newton did, except of course that his force was attractive.

Einstein's representation of gravitation by geometry is attractive, and it may well be that most of the fundamental laws of physics can be expressed in a form independent of the observer's frame of reference, though so far attempts to combine gravity and Maxwellian electrodynamics and express them in such a form have not been entirely successful, and even less so for the quantum theory.

Part of the attraction of General Relativity lies in the idea that the fundamental laws of the Universe ought to be such that they can be stated in a form independent of the frame of reference used, that there should be no arbitrary privilege. But there is one *naturally* privileged, namely that supplied by the whole material universe itself. This alternative requires the material universe to have a certain degree of symmetry. If for example our own galaxy, which is almost certainly like a disc in shape, were all that mattered, and if a frame fixed with respect to it had special validity, one would expect some kind of difference between motion in the disc and in a direction perpendicular to it. This has never been detected, apart from the motion of the sun which moves like a planet round the central bunch of stars. However, our galaxy is in fact surrounded by thousands of millions of other similar galaxies so arranged that no one direction is favoured.

In recent years this has been claimed as a fundamental principle called the Cosmological Principle, which asserts that considered on the largest scale the universe is the same in all directions, and looks roughly the same from whatever galaxy it is viewed. Though this principle is itself contested and may perhaps be disproved by study of the most distant astronomical regions by radio telescopes, if valid even in a modified form it would supply a privileged frame of reference. This would be as we have seen, an inertial frame.

General Relativity should, I feel, be treated on its merits as a theory explaining certain experimental facts, which it appears to do reasonably well, and not as something metaphysical to which all theories must conform. Special Relativity is valid, as we have seen, but within certain limits. That theory applies to a limited range of observers, namely those not subject to gravity, or in other words accelerations; when these latter occur one expects it to need modification. It is a merit that a modification is possible as much in line with its original idea as is General Relativity.

Even if General Relativity is as deeply true as its strongest supporters would claim, the relativity of spin does not mean that Galileo was wrong in insisting that the earth moved. Without allowing for its spin one cannot get an inertial frame.

We have come a long way from supposing that people would fall off the antipodes, and if differences of opinion, or at least of emphasis are still possible about space, time, and gravitation, this is an example of something common in physics. Very different points of view may lead to identical or nearly identical conclusions when translated into what can be observed. It is the observations that are closest to reality. The more one abstracts from them the more exciting indeed are the conclusions one draws and the more suggestive for further advances, but the less can one be certain that some widely different viewpoint would not do as well.

H. A. LORENTZ

ONE of the hopeful features of the present age is the close relations that subsist between the scientists of different nations. Science has always been international, and as far back as the seventeenth century the men of science of the young Royal Society had contacts both individually and collectively with their colleagues on the Continent, but international relations are much closer and more frequent now than they were fifty or a hundred years ago. There are many reasons for this, but of the human causes none was more important than Lorentz. He combined with great scientific distinction, and a linguistic ability which made him at home in English, French and German as in Dutch, a large measure of administrative ability, and above all a personality which called forth respect in all and affection in most. For many years he was President of the Solvay Conferences which were held at intervals in Brussels to discuss some topical problem in physics or chemistry. They were founded and supported by E. Solvay, the head of the famous chemical firm, and were the model for a great many of the conferences which are now so important in the lives of research physicists. Lorentz had a great gift for smoothing down the difficulties apt to arise in international meetings.

Lorentz's work derives from that of Maxwell. He solved several important questions which Maxwell had left open dealing with the reflection of light and its transmission in moving media. In an even more important advance he introduced the idea of individual equal units of charge, in fact electrons. Maxwell, and Faraday before him, had concentrated attention on the medium between the electrified and magnetized bodies and the idea of charge, first due to Benjamin Franklin, was played down as being probably of secondary importance. Lorentz with his electron theory restored it to the basic position it has held ever since.

He also adopted with alacrity Fitzgerald's hypothesis that matter contracts in the directions of its motion through the ether, so that a moving sphere would be compressed like the earth which is flatter towards the poles. On returning from a short visit to J. J. Thomson he and Mrs. Lorentz sent a present of a Dutch cheese of the usual shape inscribed 'a model of the electron'.

Though the Fitzgerald-Lorentz contraction has been abandoned in its original form with the materialist view of the ether, it served as the starting point for the 'Lorentz Transformation' which forms the mathematical basis of Special Relativity and is fundamental to all later work.

When P. Zeeman, Lorentz's pupil, discovered the effect of a magnetic field on the light from a sodium flame (Chap. III) it was to Lorentz that he turned for an explanation, which was given in a few days on the basis of the new electron theory, and formed the first estimate of the ratio of the charge to the mass of the still hypothetical electrons. The 'Zeeman effect' was afterwards one of the important tools in the study of atomic structure in the nineteen-twenties. There were other distinguished physicists in Holland at the turn of the century, notably Van der Waals, and though a small country it ranked as a Great Power in physics.

ALBERT EINSTEIN

So much has been written about Einstein that one hesitates before adding to it. His sweet and lovable character, which charmed those who knew him in his later years in Princeton, is too well known to need further remarks. So are his efforts for peace, which did not prevent him writing to Roosevelt to warn him of the importance of uranium fission, and his efforts for intellectual freedom. However, in a book such as this, which is primarily concerned with the methods of scientific discovery, a few words on his approach to physics may be helpful. His work is the supreme example of the use of mathematics as a model. In the nineteenth century physicists made mechanical models of nature, especially of atoms and of the ether. These models were based of course on Newtonian mechanics and were sometimes quite complex, sometimes no more so than a quivering blancmange. They were swept away by the success of Maxwell's electromagnetic theory which showed that the ether could not be merely mechanical. The Michelson-Morley experiment and its interpretation by Special Relativity put an end to attempts to re-invent an electrical ether. The word was abandoned in physics, and became almost indecent, though for some years now there have been signs that both word and idea are coming back into repute.

The mathematical model has taken the place of the mechanical. The extensive use is modern, though Galileo used it in a simple form, and it can not unfairly be said to be the basis of Greek cosmogony. It means selecting some attractive and elegant branch of mathematics which has some resemblance to the physical facts being studied and trying to see if in some form or another it can be made to fit, or nearly fit. It is rather as though one drew a series of ideal maps and looked round for a country that they represented. For his General Theory of Relativity Einstein used a mathematical apparatus called the tensor calculus. This is in essence geometrical, though like most modern geometry expressed in algebraic symbols. Einstein's basic idea was that gravitation is a property of the space near massive bodies, but the working out is always suggested, and sometimes dictated, by the use of the tensor calculus. The results have been described above in the barest outline, as far as can be done without mathematics.

Simplicity is so much a part of the beauty of mathematics that any mathematical theorist will always choose the simplest of the possibilities open to him that does not strongly conflict with the facts, while there seems no particular reason to suppose that the universe is simple there is good reason for assuming it to be so. If the particular aspect one is studying is truly very complex one may as well give the problem up, unless there happens to be a simple approximation close enough to the truth to be worth knowing. There seems also to be no valid reason to suppose nature mathematical, but here again progress in theory can hardly be made unless it is. In fact mathematical models have proved useful, even if Einstein's theory does not prove the last word on gravitational theory. The fascinating problems it leads to respecting the depths of space, have certainly caused considerable progress.

This way of attacking a problem is very different from that of Rutherford; yet both have this in common that an ideal picture is made of the hidden phenomena, which are likened in the one case to relations between certain mathematical quantities, in the other to that between material bodies moving in particular ways.

Einstein's work was by no means limited to relativity. Besides his early theory of the agitation of particles in liquids, he extended Planck's quantum theory to radiation in free space which he supposed to go in packets now called photons. By these he explained the paradox that feeble X-rays can eject electrons from matter as forcibly as when the X-rays are much more intense, though fewer of them. Quantity not quality changes if, for example, the piece of matter is brought nearer to the source of X-rays.

VI

MASS, ENERGY, MATTER

THE concepts of mass and energy are so important in themselves and interconnected in so interesting a fashion that they deserve a special chapter. Galileo and later Newton made the idea of mass or inertia fundamental in their mechanics. Others had asked what made objects move and given varied reasons. Galileo turned the question round and said in effect that what needs answering is why a moving body stops, if and when it does. He saw that the same property of inertia which makes it hard to move a massive body makes it hard to stop when once it is moving. The more massive the bullet the more damage it will do when it hits, speeds being equal. Galileo conceived of a force as something which changes a body's state not only of rest but of motion. Under a force a body will accelerate to a degree equal to the force divided by a number which measures the amount of material in the body, called the *mass*. In strict logic this law is only a (partial) definition of force and mass, but it was implied that 'mass' is a constant of a lump of matter which does not change unless pieces of matter are added and removed, and that the 'forces' bear some reasonable relation to circumstances outside the body on which they act. Forces might be weight, i.e. the attraction of the earth; the pull of a visible string; a magnetic force which though it acts invisibly proceeds from a visible magnet. Newton added the idea that forces are always double-ended so that action is equal to reaction between two bodies. This at once makes it possible to compare masses by making two bodies collide with one another and observing the proportion between the changes in velocity produced by action and reaction in the two bodies (it is of course quite arbitrary which end of a force is called the action and which the reaction).

It has already been explained that the weight of a body at any point of the earth's surface is proportional to its mass so that masses can be compared by weighing. Buying a pound of butter is essentially buying mass. The weight merely adds to the inconvenience of getting it home.

This concept of mass sufficed for the purposes of mechanics for 250 years and more. It seemed the most firmly grounded of physical concepts; the main property of matter, indeed almost its definition, seemed to be to have mass. The first tiny hint that all was not quite so simple was supplied in a paper by J. J. Thomson in 1881 to which I have already referred. This was an exercise on Maxwell's theory of electromagnetism, then new, which showed that if a metal sphere were electrified it would behave as though it had a small extra mass. The extra mass was too small for there to be any hope of detecting it experimentally, and even if it had been detected it could have been said that this was not real mass but only something that looked like it.

Still, people began to speak of electromagnetic mass and when the electron was discovered it was suggested that its mass might be of this nature. It was a reasonable idea because the mass calculated for a given electric charge increases as the radius of the sphere diminishes and that of an electron might well be very small indeed. Then came the discovery that the masses of electrons in the form of beta rays depend on their speeds, increasing with the speed. This is quite contrary to Newtonian ideas, but is to be expected for electromagnetic mass. The variation calculated agreed roughly with the experiment. The variation of mass only becomes appreciable when the velocity approaches that of light, but then it becomes large.

At this point we must break off the argument to return to it after considering the concept of energy. This idea was dominant in the physics of the middle nineteenth century and is associated with the names of Joule, Kelvin, Helmholtz and Clausius. One can however see a trace of it in the experiments, partly real and partly conceptual, by which Galileo arrived at the idea of mass. When a weight hanging by a string moves as a pendulum it gathers speed from rest at its highest point till at the bottom of its swing it is moving fastest. Then as it rises on the other side it slows down till it comes momentarily to rest at the same height as it started from. Galileo pointed out that if the string struck a projecting peg the motion, now in an arc of smaller radius, would yet carry the weight to the same height. The motion of the pendulum at the bottom has the power, as it gets exhausted, of raising the weight to its original height irrespective of the path. Thus

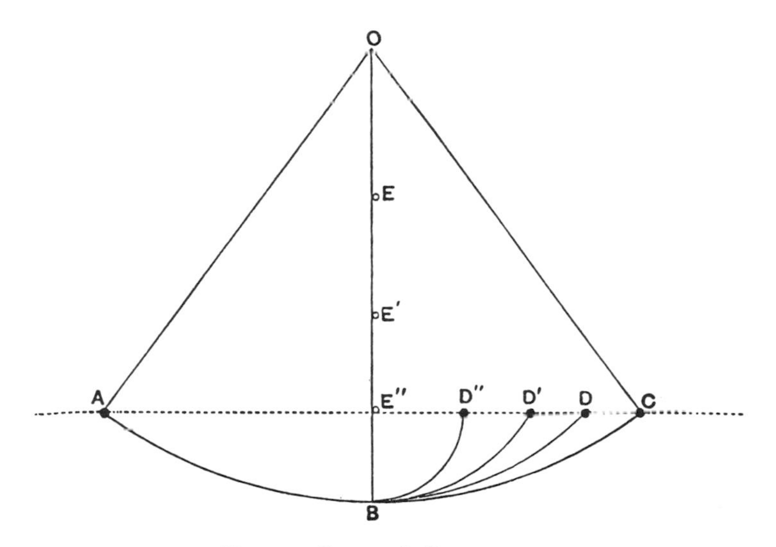

FIG. 10. GALILEO'S EXPERIMENT

A bullet is hung from the nail *O* by a thread. It is drawn aside to *A* and then released. It describes the curve *AB* which Galileo perceived may be regarded as a series of very short inclined planes of different slopes. It then reverses its motion, arriving at *C*, in the same horizontal level as *A*. Drive in a nail at *E* and repeat the experiment. After passing the vertical the thread will catch on the nail and the bullet will describe a circle *BD* with *E* as centre but will still rise to the same level *AC*. Similarly if the nail is at *E'* or *E''*.

increase of motion is associated with fall, and decrease with raising of the weight.

But what in circumstances like this is the proper measure of 'quantity of motion' or 'efficacy' as it was sometimes called? This was much discussed in the seventeenth century, some held that it is mass times velocity, others that the velocity comes in as the square, in symbols mv^2. Here m is the mass of the slowly moving particle. As usual in this kind of controversy both sides were right. It depends on how you propose to use it. Both quantities have since been given names, mass times velocity is called 'momentum' and mass times velocity squared (divided by 2 for a reason which will appear) is called 'kinetic energy'. It is the energy due to motion. Both concepts are useful because each figures in a 'conservation law', which means that there is something which does not change in the course of the operation.

The conservation of momentum can readily be shown to be an immediate consequence of Newton's law of action and reaction. It states that the total momentum of a set of bodies is unchanged in direction and magnitude by interaction between them. It applies to any system which is completely self-contained but not, for example, to a pendulum, for the weight is attracted by the earth. We should have somehow to measure the momentum given to the earth by the pull of the weight and take this into account, obviously an impractical process. On the other hand when a gun is fired the conservation of momentum tells one what the recoil will be in relation to the initial speed of the shot and the ratio of the mass as of shot and gun. In this case the weight is a relatively small force compared with the great impulse of the explosion.

Conservation for kinetic energy is slightly more complicated. It is not conserved by itself, but only when added to another quantity called 'potential energy'. This in the case of the pendulum is the height of the weight above some level multiplied by the weight. The level chosen does not matter since only *differences* come in. As the pendulum swings the energy of the bob changes gradually from all potential at the top of the swing to all kinetic at the bottom, choosing for convenience the bottom as the reference level. Calculation shows that $\frac{1}{2}mv^2$ is the right quantity to use for kinetic energy to make this happen. Now this is in a sense an arbitrary definition. One can calculate all about the motion of a pendulum without using the idea of kinetic energy. It gives one nothing new. In some more complicated problems—the motion of a planet or sputnik for example—it is a useful mathe-

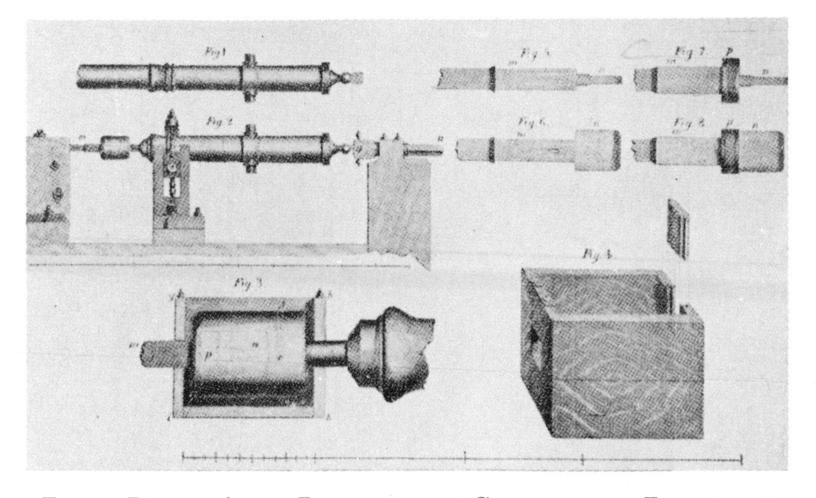

FIG. 11. RUMFORD'S OWN DRAWINGS OF HIS CANNON-BORING EXPERIMENTS

Fig. 1 shows a cannon cast with a solid block on the muzzle. A neck was turned between block and cannon which was mounted on a primitive lathe, *Fig.* 2, which could be turned by horses. A blunt borer *m* was pressed forcibly against the inside of a hole in the block, which was lagged with flannel and placed in a wooden box (*Figs.* 3 & 4).

The rise in temperature due to the friction was measured by a thermometer in the hole '*de*', *Fig.* 3. In one experiment the thermometer rose by 70° F., the weight of metal being 113 lb. Only 837 *grains* of dust were produced. The object of this experiment was to meet the objection that the sensible heat produced in cutting metal was released from the chips produced which were assumed to have a smaller capacity for heat than the bulk metal. Rumford thought that the small quantity of chips and dust for so much heat made this explanation unlikely. He also showed that the specific heat of chips is the same as of bulk metal.

matical short cut, but if this were all the importance of energy would be minor.

The conception of energy became one of the greatest in physics because it unites so many branches of physics together. For example, heat was for long thought to be an invisible fluid called 'caloric' which flowed from hot bodies to cold. But bodies can be heated far above their surroundings by friction, as first Rumford showed by boring cannon and then Joule more accurately by churning water by paddles driven by falling weights. The loss of potential energy by the falling weight is found accurately proportioned to the heat produced. No other change than in temperature occurs to the water. It is easy to see how one can make a conservation law from these facts. One need only measure heat in the right units, and then in any experiment of the kind heat plus potential energy will be constant, as potential energy decreases heat will increase by an equal amount. A bullet, to take another example, has kinetic energy, which when it is fired upwards into the air gets partly changed into potential energy. If however it is fired into a butt and brought to rest it will get very hot. This heat, when collected, is just equal to the kinetic energy destroyed. There are a great variety of experiments of this general type which fully confirm that heat is one form that energy can take. One can visualize this by thinking of a hot gas as one in which the molecules are in violent random motion, so each has its own kinetic energy, and of a hot solid as one in which atoms or molecules are rapidly oscillating about fixed positions. The energy in the latter case is partly kinetic and partly elastic. The forces holding the atoms can store energy as can the main spring of a watch.

Heat is only one form of energy among many; it would take much too long to go through the many manifestations of this entity as electrical and magnetic energy, as radiation from the sun and other hot bodies, as nuclear energy, or in chemical form as shown by the burning of coal or oil. To do so would almost be to write a textbook of physics. The essential idea is of something which can take many forms, which can be transmitted from one body to another and which when it is transformed from one manifestation to another does so at a definite rate of exchange. For example, the potential energy corresponding to the fall of a kilogramme through 100 metres will heat 236 grams of water 1 °C., or if turned completely into electrical energy will give a kilowatt of electric power for about a second. In practise, if used in a hydroelectric plant some of the energy would go into heat in the escaping water and the dynamo, and the rest, say 90 or 95%, appear as electric power.

It is now time to apply this to our colliding particles and see how, by the use of the ideas of relativity, we are led to regard mass as a kind of energy. We will choose particles which can collide without any appreciable change of kinetic energy into heat or radiation. This is an idealization which cannot be exactly reproduced experimentally with objects like billiard balls. For atomic projectiles the approximation is much better, but in any case the arguments which follow are not upset if a small loss in total kinetic energy occurs due to its changing into heat or radiation.

In such a collision there is of course a transfer of energy and of momentum from one particle to the other, but in total they are conserved. Now special relativity requires laws to be equally valid for all observers moving without acceleration with respect to one another. What happens here? If we just take the ordinary expressions mv for momentum and $\frac{1}{2}mv^2$ for kinetic energy and translate the velocities from one observer to another according to the laws which relativity gives and which differ from those of Newton, *keeping the masses unchanged*, it doesn't work. But if conservation is to mean anything physically and not just be a mathematical accident, it can have nothing to do with the observer. We seem to be in a dilemma, which would require us either to abandon the well-established conservation laws or admit that the rules for translating velocities from one observer to another given by relativity are wrong. This last would mean abandoning relativity. But there may be a way out. Perhaps we can modify the mathematical expressions mv and $\frac{1}{2}mv^2$ in such a way that the new expressions if conserved for one observer will be conserved for all when translated according to relativistic rules. The modifications must not be too drastic. We want to say that these are 'really' the right expressions for momentum and energy, but we know that the old ones work so long as velocities are much smaller than that of light. Hence the new ones must be closely similar under these conditions. The restrictions are serious but in fact it can be done. Such mathematical expressions do exist. For momentum all that is needed is to substitute for the old fixed mass a new mass varying with the speed. Indeed, the precise mathematical expression had already been suggested by Lorentz on the basis of his contraction. It differs a little from the earlier variable electromagnetic mass (p. 80) but careful experiments with beta rays showed that it was right.

This mass increases indefinitely near the speed of light in agreement with the fundamental idea of relativity that nothing can go faster than this. Any object would show indefinitely increasing inertia and so resist effectively any force that tried to drive it past that speed.

The change needed in the expression for energy is a little more drastic. One must take for the energy the new variable mass, call it M, multiplied by the square of the velocity not of the particle but of *light*, giving Einstein's famous relation $E = Mc^2$, where 'c' is the velocity of light. At first sight this does not look much like the old expression since the velocity of the particle seems to have disappeared. It hasn't really for it is included in M, and it is easy to show* that in fact it agrees approximately, except for the important fact that included in the energy is a part mc^2, m you will remember is the original mass of the particle when moving slowly, called 'rest mass' in relativity. This part, which is very large because light goes so fast, implies, if you take it seriously, that mass merely by its existence possesses energy in vast quantities.

Einstein also produced a rather similar argument to show that the absorption by a body of energy in the form of radiation would increase its mass according to the same law. These predictions remained only theoretical till very accurate measurements were

* $M = \frac{m}{\sqrt{1 - v^2/c^2}}$ is the Lorentz expression, so $Mc^2 = \frac{mc^2}{\sqrt{1 - v^2/c^2}}$

$$= mc^2 + \tfrac{1}{2}mv^2 + \tfrac{3}{8}\frac{mv^4}{c^2} + \text{etc.}$$

Now when v is much smaller than c the third and later terms can be neglected.

made by Aston of the masses of individual subspecies of atoms and it became possible to compare the mass of, for example, a radium atom with the mass of the pieces produced by its dissociation. The energy released by the explosion of a radium atom is large enough to make it possible to detect the loss in rest mass of the sum of the material fragments compared with the mass of the original atom.

With nuclear energy Einstein's relation has come into its own and is decisive in showing which nuclear reactions can be expected to release energy and which cannot. It is indeed a remarkable paradox that mass which is virtually synonymous with inertia should prove identical with energy, for this is what the law amounts to. The mass of any system is a measure of its total energy. If the energy is increased by action from outside the mass must increase *pari passu*. Such an increase will usually occur either by adding visible matter or by radiation coming in, and radiation has mass. It was in fact proved experimentally in the nineteenth century that light falling on an absorber or reflector exerts a pressure on it just as would a stream of bullets. For light of the intensity obtainable on earth the pressure is small but measurable and agrees with the predictions of Maxwell's theory. Now the exertion of pressure when motion is stopped or its direction is changed is the fundamental property of mass.

I have attempted to explain how Einstein's law was discovered, though to do so requires a mathematical argument, because it illustrates the way in which mathematics may suggest, though they cannot prove, a physical law. Here were two groups of laws, the conservation laws and those deduced from relativity, each self-consistent and well supported by experiment. As stated they were contradictory. The problem was to find some modification of one which would not be contrary to the experiments on which it was based but remove the contradiction. In the process a very important new principle was discovered. It has happened on more than one occasion that mathematical expressions adopted for convenience have suggested important conclusions later verified experimentally. Is nature really mathematical at heart or can we only discover the parts which are?

Einstein's law is sometimes taken as saying that matter is nothing but energy. I think the statement goes too far. Ordinary matter is associated with certain elementary units, electrons, protons, neutrons and perhaps some others which have at least a high degree of permanence. These units are centres of mass, and most of the energy of any ordinary object is the sum of the 'rest masses' of these units. Actually the energy is usually substantially less than this since much energy must have been released when the heavier atoms were formed, as we believe they were, from primitive electrons and protons. But the particles are something more than mere centres of mass. For one thing electrons and protons have electric charge. All three have built-in magnetic moments and intrinsic spins like tops. They are entities with definite properties.

One reason which has lent force to the idea that matter is only energy is that it is possible, as Blackett and Chadwick showed, to create electrons from radiation. When this is done one never gets a single electron but always a *pair*, one normal negatively charged electron and one positive electron, which later disappears in a suicide pact a short time later with some negative electron. This pair production is a definite phenomenon predicted theoretically by Dirac. It also happens with protons, as has been shown recently in the laboratory at Berkeley, California. In this case since the original proton has a positive charge, the new 'anti-proton' has a negative one. The anti-proton later disappears by annihilation with a normal proton and release of energy.

These processes look very like the creation of matter from energy, but there are recent experiments which at least hint in the opposite direction. When the primary cosmic rays from outer space strike the atmosphere a variety of unstable particles are produced which were discovered by the tracks they make in photographic plates and in cloud chambers. The action of the primary cosmic rays can now be imitated by the great proton accelerators, such as the Bevatron at Berkeley, the Cosmotron at Brookhaven and the international machine at the *CERN* laboratory near Geneva, though nature still wins in producing the highest energies. There are a great variety of these particles;

including the old ones such as negative and positive electrons; twenty-six are known, with a fair possibility that there are at least a few more yet to come. Among these particles are several pairs of particles and anti-particles. The particles fall into three groups, the first group consists of particles whose number is *not* conserved, such as the photons which form ordinary light and certain particles called mesons which are connected with the nuclear forces: second, a group of particles related to electrons called for brevity leptons: third, a group called baryons related to protons. It should be mentioned here that neutrons, though apparently stable in nuclei, transform themselves when free in about twenty minutes into protons, releasing electrons and another particle called a neutrino.

Now the rule which is suggested, and for which there is a good deal of evidence, though it can hardly be said to be established yet, is that these last two groups are fundamentally different and that the numbers of each separately are conserved, with one important proviso. Namely that when an 'anti-particle' is produced it counts negative. Thus a pair of electrons, particle and anti-particle, can be produced from a photon only. The photon counts as zero for purposes of conservation being in our first group. The negative electron counts 1 and the positive −1, so the sum is zero. Similarly for the decay of a neutron, the electron produced is 'cancelled' by the neutrino which must in this case be an anti-neutrino. The neutron and proton are each baryons, and there is no change here. Clearly one can force the facts, up to a point, into a law of this kind by suitable choice of what is 'anti-particle' and what 'particle', but one must of course be consistent, and when as is now the case there are quite a large number of transformations known it becomes significant that the assignment can be made in a consistent way.

Assuming that further research establishes this rule, it means that matter is composed of two classes of entity, each of which can exist with various masses. Thus the neutrino or antineutrino has a 'rest mass' very much less than that of an electron, probably indeed zero, though both are leptons. A particle with zero rest mass has also zero energy by Einstein's law, *except* when it goes with the velocity of light when it can have any energy and the corresponding mass. This is not just a mathematical quibble as to the result of multiplying zero by infinity but a necessary assumption for the theory of light (Chapter IX), though here the particle of zero rest mass is the photon not the neutrino. Leptons and baryons are then separate entities which may, and indeed usually do, have rest masses assigned to them, but not necessarily so and not always the same mass when they do. For example the mass of a neutron slightly exceeds that of a proton, though both are baryons, and leptons called mu mesons are known with a mass 207 times that of an electron.

Mass in fact becomes only one among several properties which the primitive units of matter can have. Perhaps it is not even the most fundamental, for the masses of these new particles show very odd ratios not fitting any simple law, while their charges are either -1, $+1$, or 0 in terms of that of an electron and their spins are small integral multiples of a unit. It almost looks as though the masses are only consequences of something more fundamental.

Though mass is energy, and rest mass usually the greatest part of the energy of a material system, matter is something more.

The relation of rest mass to charge remains mysterious. On relativistic grounds theoretical physicists do not like assigning a definite radius to an electron or proton, but if they are considered as points their rest mass becomes infinite. Means have been devised for handling the mathematics and getting reasonable answers, but the position is unsatisfactory.

VII

HOW CERTAIN DISCOVERIES WERE MADE

THE discovery of the electron and of the atomic nucleus are examples of discoveries which provided solutions for long-standing problems, in the first case the double problem of the nature of cathode rays and of the unitary character of electric charges, in the second the nature of the massive positively charged part of the atom. But this kind of discovery is not the only way by which physics advances and it may be of interest to describe two important discoveries which were less the solutions of puzzles than the discovery of unsuspected effects. These are Röntgen's discovery of X-rays and the proof by Hess of the existence of cosmic rays. To these we will add Rayleigh's discovery of argon as an example of one due to accurate measurement.

On the 8th of November in the year 1895 Professor Wilhelm Conrad Röntgen of the University of Würzburg was working alone in the private room of his laboratory studying the discharge produced by an induction coil in an exhausted tube of the kind known as a Crookes tube. He had covered this with thin black cardboard, and near it lay a screen of paper covered with barium platinocyanide crystals. As he turned on the discharge he was amazed to see the screen light up with fluorescence. His surprise was due not to the fact that the screen could fluoresce, for he had prepared it with that object, but that it should do so when no known form of radiation could reach it. For the next eight weeks he worked very hard, alone, and on 28 December handed the result to the Secretary of the Physico-Medical Society of Würzburg. The paper was printed at once and off-prints sent to well-known physicists and medical men. Within a matter of days Röntgen's results were being repeated in laboratories throughout the civilized world, and in a few weeks attempts were made to use the new method of investigation as an aid to surgeons.

The new rays caught the popular imagination and figured in *Punch*, *La Nature* and *Life*, as well as in more serious journals. Never before or since has a strictly scientific discovery become famous so quickly, the nearest rival would be the discovery of nuclear fission in the last days of 1938, but the outside world was slower then to realize the possibilities.

THE NEW PHOTOGRAPHIC DISCOVERY.

THANKS TO THE DISCOVERY OF PROFESSOR RÖNTGEN, THE GERMAN EMPEROR WILL NOW BE ABLE TO OBTAIN AN EXACT PHOTOGRAPH OF A "BACKBONE" OF UNSUSPECTED SIZE AND STRENGTH!

Reproduced from PUNCH, January 25 1896.

Röntgen's first paper was a model of clear experimenting. By very simple means he established that the rays penetrated matter to a degree dependent only on the density, that they were emitted from the region where the cathode rays of the Crookes tube hit the wall, or (later) a target of platinum sealed into the tube for the purpose, that besides affecting barium platinocyanide and other fluorescent substances they would make a photographic plate developable, that they were not refracted by a prism or lens and could pass through a powder without being scattered as light would have been in powdered glass, but that there was some reflection from a dense substance. He also established the very important result that unlike cathode rays, X-rays, as he named them, were not deflected even by a strong magnetic field. They travelled in straight lines and hence an obstacle could be made to cast a sharp shadow. He suggested that they might be longitudinal vibrations of the ether. The vibrations of all known kinds of light are of course transverse, like the vibrations of a string as contrasted with the longitudinal movements in the waves of sound in air.

In a second paper communicated in March he described experiments proving that the rays made gases conducting. This important effect was discovered simultaneously and independently in Cambridge and in Paris.

Röntgen was fifty years old at the time of his discovery, and though he had published forty-nine papers none of them had been on gaseous discharge. His interests seem to have been more in fluorescence, and he is reported to have said that the reason for the barium platinocyanide screen was that he hoped to compare its fluorescence with that of an organic compound used by Lenard for detecting cathode rays sent into the atmosphere through a thin metal window. However, the tube with which the discovery was made did not have such a window. It seems probable that Röntgen, who had just started work in the field, was repeating the experiments of other workers with a Crookes tube which is more robust and easier to handle than that needed for Lenard's experiment. Lenard rays made the air visible for a few centimetres but were supposed to produce electrical effects at a greater distance, an effect actually due to X-rays which are produced in small amounts at the same time. Röntgen told a visitor a few months later that he intended to look for 'invisible radiation',* presumably connected with the Lenard rays. In this sense he may be said to have found what he was looking for,

* Glasser, *Wilhelm Conrad Röntgen*, p. 33. 1933.

though the presence of the screen near the blackened tube was a piece of luck.

Lenard had covered his tubes with black paper, probably in order to see better the rather faint light from his rays. Röntgen is said* to have done this also and it is obviously a sensible thing to do if you are looking for feeble luminosities. So Röntgen blackened his Crookes tube. Without this he would hardly have made the discovery, firstly because it would have been harder to see the fluorescence, probably rather feeble, and secondly because the fluorescence would have been attributed to the ultra-violet light known to come from discharge tubes, but this would not go through black cardboard.

Röntgen deserved his discovery for two reasons, firstly his willingness to enter a fresh and promising field off his own line of work and secondly his quickness in realizing that the glowing screen meant something out of the ordinary. That this last was something of an achievement is shown by the people who failed to make the discovery. Lenard and Hertz, who noticed the electrical effect of Lenard rays might have made it, though the hint was not so clear as was the fogging of photographic plates noticed by several workers with discharge tubes. One Oxford physicist† noticed the connection and merely removed his plates to a place of safety! Crookes, a very fine experimenter, at first attributed the fogging to defective plates, and when the manufacturers convinced him to the contrary tried improving the atmospheric conditions where the plates were kept before use. He would have got it in the end, but Röntgen forestalled him.

Without disparaging Röntgen it is fair to say that he had luck, not only in making the discovery at all but in its being so much more important both in its applications and its scientific significance than anyone could reasonably have expected. It forms indeed an epoch, dividing the old physics from the new, the physics of continuity from that of discontinuous units, electrons, quanta, and the like, but of course the division though convenient is far from sharp. The discovery of X-rays undoubtedly helped

* Glasser, *Wilhelm Conrad Röntgen*, p. 33. 1933.
† Whittaker, *History of the Theories of Aether and Matter*. Vol. II, p. 358. 1951.

that of electrons and by providing an easy means of making a gas conducting was a most effective tool in the making of further discoveries, but in these Röntgen took little part. He went back to the study of fluorescent solids as such. It is perhaps not entirely a coincidence that this revolutionary discovery owed more than usual to chance. When a field is really novel, when it is connected to the known by a very narrow door, so to speak, it will give only very few indications to the searchers who are therefore unlikely to find it by reason unhelped by luck.

To many people science is a matter of measurements carried out with meticulous accuracy. Such measurements play a great role in developing a discovery but they are rather rarely its cause. However, an example to the contrary is worth giving.

In 1892 Lord Rayleigh started a determination of the density of the gas nitrogen. By density is meant mass per unit volume and since gases are highly compressible, standard conditions of pressure and temperature have to be established for the measurement to have any significance. However, when this is done the comparison of the densities of gases is equivalent to a comparison of the weights of their molecules. In 1892, Rayleigh was simply concerned with making an accurate measurement to compare with others he had recently made on hydrogen and on oxygen.

Nitrogen is, of course, the major constituent of the atmosphere. The gas is tolerably inert and Rayleigh produced it, as was the custom, by removing chemically the other known constituents of the atmosphere, namely oxygen, carbon dioxide and water vapour. The result agreed with the density found by previous workers and most people would have left it at that. But Rayleigh thought it worth while trying another method of preparation in which part of the nitrogen came from ammonia and part from the air. The density prepared this way was slightly smaller than before; the difference was persistent. After trying several modifications of each method which made no difference, Rayleigh began to think that nitrogen from the air might be different from nitrogen from ammonia. He therefore tried a method by which *all* the nitrogen in one sample came from ammonia. This sample had a substantially lower density than any before. The difference from the atmosphere nitrogen was about four times as great as before and the effect which had been marginal became undeniable, but it was another matter to explain it. One or both might be impure but it was extraordinary that the amount of the hypothetical impurity should be so persistent. At last Rayleigh decided to try to purify the nitrogen from the air by making it combine with oxygen by prolonged sparking. This method had been used a century before by Cavendish who, as Rayleigh found when he looked up the paper, had not been able to get rid of a small residue of less than one per cent. of the initial value of gas even by very prolonged treatment. The method is now used on a giant scale for the manufacture of nitrates from the air. But Rayleigh's apparatus, though much better than that of Cavendish, was terribly slow. However, he too got a small residue. With great trouble enough of the residue was prepared to establish its properties. It was found to be much denser than nitrogen in ratio 40:28 and chemically quite inert, it received the name of 'argon', the idle one.

Sir William Ramsey, who had helped in the latter part of this work and shown how to absorb the nitrogen with magnesium, got enough nitrogen to show that its weight agreed with that of nitrogen from ammonia. He carried on the work and was able to identify three other gases neon, krypton, and xenon mixed in small quantities with the argon, and all inert. He also found that gases released from certain minerals and supposed to be nitrogen had an optical spectrum identical with certain unknown lines that Lockyer had previously observed in the sun and assigned to a hypothetical element 'helium'.

All these substances are elements, and form a complete group, the inert gases. Apart from technical uses in gas-filled incandescent lamps and in discharge tubes for coloured lights, these gases have been most important in pure science. We have already met helium as a product of radium, and neon played a great part in the history of the discovery of isotopes. But it is perhaps worth noting that Rayleigh's accuracy of measurement was needed because he had to establish the reality of the difference between two nearly equal quantities, namely the difference between the density of pure nitrogen and that of nitrogen containing about one per cent. of argon (with a great deal less of the other inert gases). The accurate value of a physical quantity is not often of much importance in itself, but great accuracy may be needed where the significant quantity is a *difference*.

Our next discovery shall be an example of the great consequences which can follow the close study of a small unexplained effect. As the early work was done with quite simple apparatus one can follow the experiments more closely than in most cases. Most people have seen a gold leaf electroscope (Fig. 13). When electrified by touching with, for example, a vulcanite rod rubbed on cat's skin the leaf stands away from its support because the like (negative) charges on the leaf and the support repel one another. If left for a time the leaf will gradually collapse on to the support. The charge has leaked away. This may be because the insulation of the support is defective and conducts the charge to earth, but even in the eighteenth century it was believed that this was not the whole story, and that even with the best insulation charge was slowly conducted away by the air.

After Bequerel, stimulated by the discovery of X-rays, found that uranium salts emitted rays which made the air round them a conductor, as well as affecting a photograph plate, this natural conduction of the air received a good deal of attention. Following a theory which had proved successful in studying the conductivity produced by X-rays, it was supposed that the rays had the power of splitting a few of the molecules of the air each into two parts called ions, one positively and the other negatively charged. If for example the electroscope had a negative charge it would attract up positive ions which would neutralize its charge. The negative ions would be repelled away.

By a simple device (Fig. 13) one can arrange that leakage over the support is prevented, and one can then treat the measured rate of collapse as an indication of the number of ions present. Experiments in the open air were erratic. When the device was put into a closed vessel it was found that the rate of collapse was greater in a large than in a small vessel. This is because more ions will, in general, be produced in the larger vessel and the

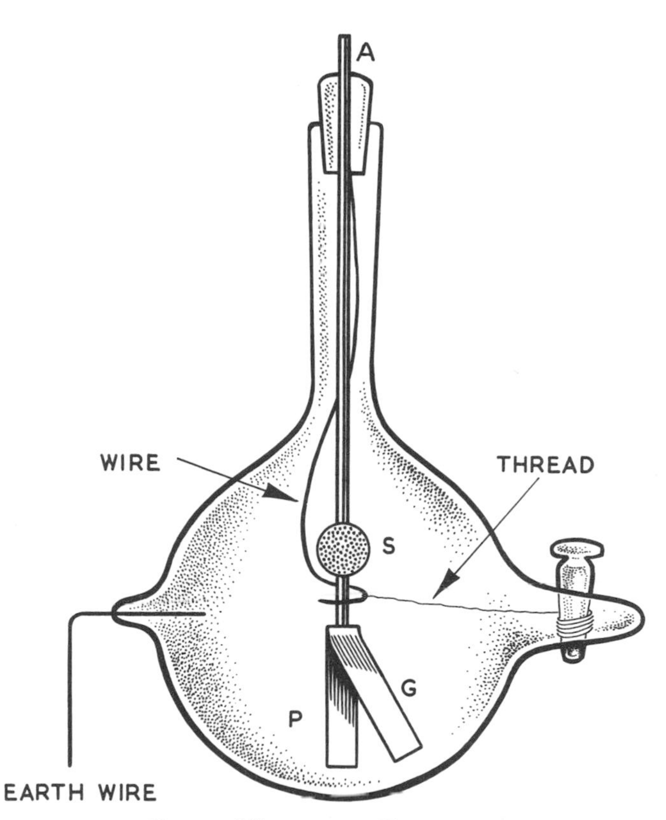

FIG. 13. WILSON-TYPE ELECTROSCOPE

The rod *A* has a piece of sulphur *S* melted on to its end, at the other side of *S* is attached a plate *P* and a piece of gold leaf loosely hinged to it. A wire connects *A* and *P* while the electroscope is being charged by connecting *A* to one pole of a battery. The like charges on *P* and *G* make *G* move away from *P* as shown. Contact between *A* and *P* is then broken by pulling the wire away with a thread. Leak from *G* across the air to earth will make *G* fall slowly. Any leak *across S from A to P* has the opposite effect. The inside of the vessel is made feebly conducting.

conditions are supposed adjusted so that all, or virtually all, of those of the right sign reach the gold leaf.

The size of the effect varies a good deal with what the apparatus is made of, but taking no special precautions one might get about 20 ion pairs per cubic centimetre per sec. This sounds quite a lot till one realizes that a cubic centimetre of air at atmospheric pressure and ordinary temperature contains $2 \cdot 7 \times 10^{19}$ molecules. This is roughly the total population of our galaxy if every one of the ten thousand million (or so) stars in it has a planet with the same population as the earth! That one can detect and measure a process which breaks up only 20 of these per second shows the extraordinary sensitiveness of electrical detection.

Though uranium, which gives rise to radium, is among the rarer elements it is widely spread in small quantities and most rocks contain a detectable amount, so radiation from the walls of the laboratory accounts for quite a fraction of the 20. If the laboratory had been used for experiments in radioactivity it would probably be contaminated, especially in the early days when the danger from the emanations was not understood. These are gases, released from radium itself and two other radioactive substances, which after a time break down to form on any surface near by a radioactive deposit likely to give trouble for twenty years or more.

It was found that the ionization could be reduced by shielding the electroscope with a good thickness of lead, but after a certain point no change occurred by making the lead thicker. The first result could be explained as the lead absorbing radiations from the walls and ground (these are mostly the penetrating 'gamma' radiation), the second required either a radiation more penetrating than those from known radiation substances or perhaps radioactive impurities in the lead. Electroscopes made of different metals gave different results, presumably because of different amounts of radioactive impurity. But was it all due to impurity? Might there not be a natural radioactivity of all or most kinds of atoms, obviously very small, but the same in kind to that shown by the very heavy elements uranium, thorium, and their products? It was hopes of discovering this that led a number of

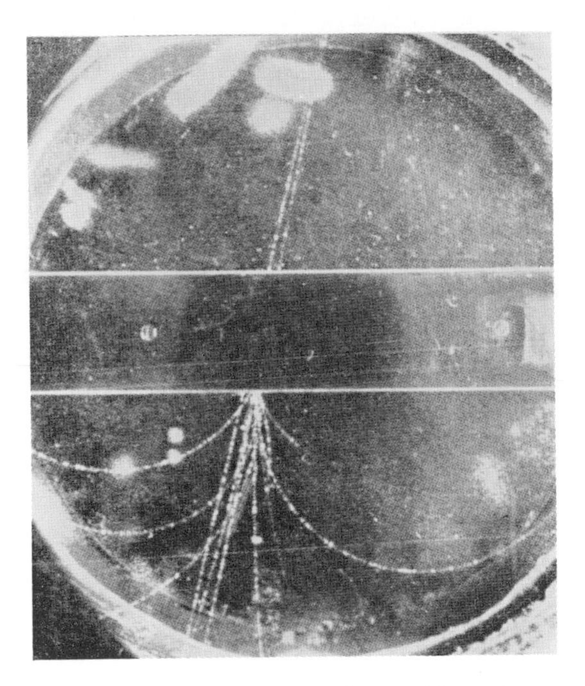

FIG. 14. COSMIC RAYS IN A WILSON CHAMBER

Two cosmic rays come in from above and go into a thick horizontal lead plate which divides the chamber in two. One is a mu-meson and goes right through, the other is an electron and produces several pairs of positive and negative electrons either directly or with photons as an intermediate stage. The chamber is in a magnetic field which bends the positive and negative electrons in opposite direction. The initial rays are going too fast to show any visible bending.

experimenters to continue work in this field, even after C. S. Wright, who afterwards went with Scott to the Antarctic, had shown by measurements on the ice on Lake Ontario that the ionization rate could be pushed as low as 4·4 ions per cc. per sec.

A number of experiments were made on towers to get away from the radiation from radioactivity in the ground. Here the difficulties were that the bricks of the tower might receive 'active deposit' from the emanation sucked from the ground when the barometer falls. There was a definite decrease with height, but there still remained a residuum.

Not long before World War I a group in Austria had the idea of trying the effect in a balloon. The first flights were inconclusive, they showed a decrease in ionization for the first 1,000 feet or so, but less than expected. The ionization chambers used must have been rather badly contaminated for the minimum was not nearly so low as that found by Wright. This made the results hard to interpret. At last, however, Hess got a really high flight to 5,000 feet and confirmed, what had been suspected before, that the ionization actually increased at great heights and indeed to a substantial extent. There was only one explanation and Hess gave it. Some kind of radiation must be coming down from above, and the excess high up is due to its being absorbed by the air as it descends. This marks the discovery of cosmic rays.

A vast amount of work has been done since then on these rays. They are of great complexity, chiefly due to the many changes these rays suffer in going through the air. I will only say enough to give a hint of the importance of Hess's discovery. The original rays are now known to consist of the nuclei of the atoms up to at least iron in atomic number, but with protons in the great majority and helium nuclei (i.e. alpha particles) next. They have energies—at least those that reach the top of the atmosphere—ranging from 100 million to 10^{16} volts* or more. The biggest particle accelerator now working, that at Geneva (run by the

* It is customary in atomic physics to reckon energies in volts, i.e. the energy which a singly charged particle would be given by moving through a difference of potential of so many volts.

Centre European de Researche Nucleare), gives protons an energy of about 25 billion volts. These would be very moderate cosmic rays. It is still uncertain where the rays are produced, or how, but it is very likely that some, at least, come from the huge explosions known as supernovae of which one occurs in our galaxy every two or three centuries. A few of the feebler ones sometimes come from the sun during the storms called solar flares but this is not an important source.

In the collisions that these particles make with the nuclei of the atoms forming the air the latter are broken up and so are the rays themselves except for those that start as protons which cannot be changed. These collisions result in the production of a great deal of energetic radiation of the extreme X-ray type which in turn produces electrons and positrons by pair production (p. 87). Most of the radiation at moderate heights consists of these. More interesting products from the theoretical point of view are the various kinds of mesons and 'strange particles'. These are neither atom, proton, neutrons nor electrons yet are called elementary particles since they are not the result of unions of anything else. They have masses ranging from some 200 times that of an electron to about $1\frac{1}{2}$ times that of a proton. They are all more or less unstable changing spontaneously into one of the group; electron (including positron), proton, or neutron. Each change involves a diminution in rest mass, some changes involve a division into two or more particles of this general kind. Superfluous energy comes off as kinetic energy, as ordinary electromagnetic energy (X-rays) or as neutrinos. These last are particles of zero electric charge and zero rest mass invented by Pauli to explain peculiarities in the production of β rays and almost undetectable. For long they were regarded with some suspicion, as a device for saving the face of the conservation of energy but, like many innovations, grew more respectable with time and recently have been fully established by detecting the effects of the vast swarm of neutrinos (strictly speaking of anti-neutrinos) produced in a nuclear reactor.

Some mesons are believed to be intimately concerned with nuclear forces. The 'strange particles' have led to the ideas about leptons and baryons described on p. 88.

All this has been found out because people suspected that the leaking of electroscopes was not fully accounted for by the effects which they already knew. They hoped to discover universal radioactivity, which in fact does not exist, though three or four medium-weight elements do radiate feebly, notably potassium which in our bodies supplies an appreciable fraction of the radiation we all receive. In fact these few exceptions are not of much theoretical importance, not to be compared with the discoveries made through the study of cosmic rays. In order to make great discoveries it is not necessary to know what one is going to discover. This is rather rare; but it is most important to have a good nose for the important discrepancy.

JOHN WILLIAM STRUTT, third BARON RAYLEIGH (1842–1919)

was an outstanding example of a group of men to whom science in this country owes a great deal, the serious amateurs. Men who devoted their lives to science without pay and without the stimulus of competition that comes from being a member of a recognized profession. Rayleigh was indeed for five years Cavendish Professor at Cambridge, but this was merely an episode, most of his experimental work was done in a small laboratory with a single assistant in his country house at Terling in Essex.

But though an amateur he was certainly not an idle one. His *Collected Papers* include 446 items and his *Theory of Sound* is still consulted. It is sometimes said that Rayleigh was the last man who 'knew physics'. This is perhaps doubtful, but he was the last who made substantial contributions to every branch of the subject known when he was young. The work on argon described in this chapter was probably the peak of his scientific career, but it stood out only a little from the extraordinary high level of his work, which included the explanation of the blue of the sky and clearing up the mistakes in early determinations of the fundamental electrical units which were up to three per cent. in error. Rayleigh, who was a Senior Wrangler, had to learn the art of experiment by himself, but was equally distinguished in both theory and experiment.

It has generally been found that mathematicians, like poets, do their best work when young, and quite a number who have achieved great things in youth have failed to produce anything important after the early thirties. Rayleigh maintained his output of first-rate work into the seventies. In science, as in literature, one can make a rough division between the romantics and those who follow a classical tradition. Rayleigh was definitely among the latter. Rather few original papers are read much more than ten years after they are written. By that time, if successful, their main contents have been incorporated into textbooks, the details have been improved upon, and there is little reason for re-reading them except for those interested in the history of science. Rayleigh's papers, especially the theoretical ones, are still read and quoted. This is partly because he wrote so well and clearly that his papers are a pleasure to read, and partly because he was so thorough that there is little more to be said after he has dealt with a subject.

Rayleigh married a sister of Arthur Balfour; another sister, Mrs. Sidgwick, collaborated with him in one of his papers and Balfour was called in to help with the measurements on occasions. Science was a less formal affair in those days.

In spite of his scientific work Rayleigh went a good deal into society and was well known as a raconteur. None of his recorded stories deal with physics but the following has a scientific tinge:

'At ——, a lady's maid who was late in answering the bell excused herself by saying that she forgot herself as she was so much interested in a discussion going on below as to whether we were all descended from Darwin.'

Rayleigh's eldest son and successor in the title was himself a physicist. He is best known for his work on the age of the earth, or rather of certain radioactive minerals and rocks whose age he determined from measurements of the helium accumulated in the mineral by the alpha rays from the radioactive elements.

VIII

THE TACTICS OF EXPERIMENT

EXPERIMENTS are of different kinds and vary in the course of a research. The earlier ones are likely to be highly tentative, aimed at discovering the kind of thing that is happening without much attempt at accuracy, they help to give the experimenter the general feel of the phenomena with which he is dealing. He gets to know the kind of things that matter, e.g. how important is it that the materials are pure, and how pure they must be. This is by no means an easy thing to find out, for in some cases excessively minute amounts of impurity matter; thus in semi-conductors used to make transistors impurities are reckoned in parts in a billion and are highly significant at that. In many more ordinary cases one may expect that a one per cent. impurity will make not more than a few per cent. difference to the answer. Of course, if you are working in a field that has been fairly well explored this kind of thing will be already known. As the research proceeds you will get more and more idea of what it is all about, and you will probably have some unexpected results which do not fit with pre-conceived ideas. This may be because the preconceived ideas are wrong, but it is more likely to be because the actual set-up of the apparatus is in some way different from what you suppose it to be. There is a leak or a bad contact, or a surface has got contaminated. Very, very rarely, none of these things have happened, and then perhaps you have made a discovery.

There are a few practical considerations which apply to many physical researches and though not of great theoretical importance they help towards success. In the first place, as has already been indicated, an experimental research is a struggle between the pertinacity of the experimenter and the perversity of matter. When an apparatus is first set up it practically never works. This is usually due to one or more trivial errors such as faulty connections. When these have been remedied one gets some sort of an effect, usually feeble and blurred. Then comes the process of getting the apparatus to work properly. This is done by making minor changes, sometimes only in adjustment, sometimes structural. It is very remarkable how patient work will gradually improve the behaviour of an apparatus, sometimes without one's being able to say with certainty what one has done to make the improvement. Eventually either the thing works well enough to give useful results or one comes to the conclusion that the design is radically wrong and has to tear it down and start again.

There is a considerable difference in tactics between experiments of the exploratory type designed to get a general idea of how a particular effect works, or even made in the hopes of discovering a new effect, and experiments in which it is desired to study closely and accurately effects whose general character is already well known. In the former case especially it is most important to arrange as wide a display of the results as possible. Do not be content for example with merely recording the currents in a few meters if you can arrange to show the same results as patterns on the screen of a cathode ray oscillograph—rather like a television screen. It may be that the actual things you measure will be the same, but the advantage of a display in the two dimensions of a screen or (in suitable experiments) on a photographic plate, or even by simply examining the colours of an electrical discharge, is that you get a lot of seemingly redundant information. It is, however, redundant only if the apparatus is working in the general way that your theory of it requires. If, as is quite likely, it is doing something entirely different the otherwise redundant information will show it up, and save you from a definitely erroneous interpretation. The wider display enables one to know that what ought *not* to be there is actually not there. Often the wider display carries the disadvantages of a certain loss of accuracy. This loss should normally be accepted. Only when the phenomena are well understood can one afford to go for accuracy, doing this prematurely is apt to lead to blunders. Even when everything seems well under control it is advisable to retain if possible some kind of monitoring device with a wide display to make sure that all is still going as it should.

The importance of accuracy in physics is often exaggerated.

Speaking very roughly accuracy much better than 1 per cent. only matters when one is interested in a *difference*, as Rayleigh was with his measurements of the density of nitrogen (*see* Chap. VI) and as Aston was in his precision measurements of the masses of atoms, where the small differences from integers (on a certain scale) measured the energy content of the atoms.

One general principle is of great importance in the design of experiments: *cleanness*. By this I do not mean physical cleanness, though of course this is of great moment too, but arranging so that the effect one is interested in is not cluttered up by irrelevancies. This is obvious enough but often hard to achieve. One so often finds that the quality in question gets averaged before it is recorded and all the finer details disappear in the process.

For example, conclusions of the greatest importance for atomic physics have come from a study of fast-moving particles of atomic or sub-atomic size with atoms at rest (*see* p. 48). The ideal is to record the details of the collision of one particle with one target atom or its nucleus, to observe the path of the oncoming particle and the separate paths of the scattered particle and of the target either whole or in fragments. This is sometimes possible using the techniques of the Wilson cloud chamber or photographic plates capable of recording atomic tracks. Failing this, the next best thing is to limit the target atoms to such a thin layer that the oncoming particles will each make only one effective collision. Here there is some smudging; one cannot associate a particular scattered particle with a particular kind of fragment from the target (even supposing the detector can distinguish between original particles and target fragments) but one may learn a good deal. The worst is to have a thick target, so that each particle makes a number of collisions. It will be scattered many times at random up and down, right and left, and the final effect depends more on chance than on the characteristics of the collision. Little can be learnt from such an experiment except an overall measure of the average scattering power of the target. Yet such experiments are tempting because usually easier to make than the clean ones; the targets do not have to be excessively thin and there is plenty of scattering to measure.

It is one of the standard rules of experimenting that one should change only one condition at a time, otherwise there will be confusion and it will be impossible to assign the observed difference to a definite cause. This is of course perfectly sound and easy enough to apply when all one can do is to change the settings of a few knobs, then turn one at a time! But in other cases it may not be so easy. For example if the experiment is on the electric current through a rarified gas one cannot change the pressure of the gas without changing *either* the current *or* the voltage that drives it. The same voltage will not cause the same current at different pressures. Similarly if one wants to change the nature of the gas one could either use the new gas at the same pressure *or* at a pressure which gives the same current with unchanged voltage, but not both. In practice the only real way of dealing with a case like this is to vary each quantity over as wide a range as possible, but this means doing a lot of experiments.

Actually the rule of changing only one condition at a time does not always give the best results. This is especially true for biological experiments, for example in agriculture. Experiments on, say, the effect of fertilizer show pretty wide fluctuations due to a variety of random uncontrolled causes. To get accurate results one must make a careful statistical analysis of a number of experiments, such experiments are expensive and one wants to get the most out of them that is possible. In practice a number of plots treated in different ways have to be compared, and while for statistics it is desirable to have as many as possible, against this is the fact that the larger the area which has to be used the greater is the variation in the quality of the soil, which of course must be eliminated as much as possible from the answer. R. A. Fisher has studied very carefully the planning of such experiments to get the maximum of reliable information from a given experimental effort. In most cases where two (or more) variables have to be considered, e.g. to find the best of several fertilizers to use with several possible varieties of corn, Fisher finds the best method is to make one comprehensive experiment with plots of different varieties treated with different fertilizer, rather than do a number of separate experiments on each variety. It is not merely more efficient in time and money but can be made to supply more varied information.

But when all is said and done the most important factor making for success in research is to try the right things. At any one time in a scientific subject there are a few growing points or buds where progress is likely to occur. These are the places to make for, and the skill consists in recognizing them before too many other people have seen them and spoilt things. Occasionally of course there is a real new breakthrough with virtually nothing to herald it, as in Röntgen's and Rayleigh's discoveries. Here the element of luck is considerable, though these are perhaps the discoveries that count most as they open up such fresh fields.

One must not expect too much, for each success there will be many failures, or semi-failures, where only some pedestrian facts reward one's efforts. But though luck is so important, if a man goes on trying promising things throughout a working life-time he is really unlucky if he does not get one good thing. So many people are content to work in mines where the ore is steadily getting poorer. Just occasionally of course they break through and find a new and paying seam, but it is rather rare, and more often done by the new-comer to the field with a fresh point of view.

C. T. R. WILSON (1869–1960)

who lived to a vigorous and much-loved ninety, was one of the early group at the Cavendish Laboratory. He started his research career with work on the formation of clouds, a phenomenon with which he was very familiar, as he was fond of climbing the Scottish hills. In a sense he never really left this fascinating study and it led him into very curious and exciting paths. First of all his discovery of how drops of water form by preference on the small electrified ions caused, as we now know, either by cosmic rays or terrestrial radiation, became the basis of J.J.T.'s method of measuring the charge on ions produced by X-rays (p. 34). Next he made use of the same discovery to devise the 'Wilson Chamber' in which the track of an ionizing particle through moist air could be made visible by suddenly cooling the air, causing the moisture to condense on the individual ions which thus became visible and could be photographed. The necessary uniform cooling was achieved by sudden expansion of the moist air. These cloud chambers have been one of the most important tools in atomic physics and have done more than anything else to make atoms, electrons and other such particles seem real. Wilson was a

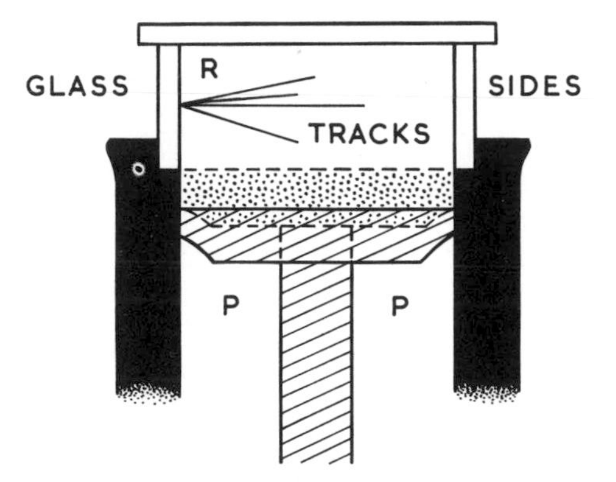

FIG. 15. SECTION OF THE EXPANSION CHAMBER IN C. T. R. WILSON'S APPARATUS FOR OBSERVING THE TRACKS OF ALPHA RAYS

The Piston *PP* is dropped suddenly from the position indicated by the dotted lines to the position indicated by the full lines; so that the air in the expansion chamber is suddenly chilled by the expansion, and fog settles on the tracks of the helium atoms shot out by the radium at *R*.

wonderful experimenter. He had his fill of Scottish caution and worked very slowly, making most of the apparatus himself. The classic story about him, true in spirit if not in fact, is that 'X' said good-bye to him grinding a plate of glass in his room in the Cavendish. Three years later 'X' returned and C.T.R. was still grinding the plate. 'Yes,' said he when told, 'but it was another plate.' He only did a few experiments in his life, but each worth the whole output of most other men. He was, it must be said, one of the world's worst lecturers, but an excellent teacher to a single pupil, for which I have good reason to be grateful, and skilled at designing experiments for teaching.

He was slight in build, with a keen thin face, and a strong Scottish accent.

IX

THE QUEER BEHAVIOUR OF THE VERY SMALL

In this chapter it seems best, after a short account of waves, to state certain conclusions first and then the reasons which led to them. These conclusions are frankly contrary to common sense, but I can assure readers that this weird solution was not arrived at without much difficulty and not without trying a great variety of alternative ideas, none of which stood up to the test of experiment. By very small I shall normally mean electrons, the lightest of the particles with which we have to deal, but protons and whole atoms are not, in this respect, fundamentally different from electrons; it is merely that their greater mass makes them less susceptible to the peculiar behaviour we shall be discussing. It is a matter of degree, but while this peculiarity is striking in the case of electrons it is detectable with some difficulty in the case of atoms and merely theoretical for anything much bigger. For many purposes photons, though not permanent entities like electrons, behave in the same way as they do.

As waves are fundamental to these ideas I hope the reader will allow me a short digression on them. The most familiar waves are, of course, those on water, but the waves produced on the sea by wind are usually very irregular and do not bring out the characteristic properties as much as one might hope. Two other important classes of waves are those of sound and those which carry radio. Sound waves are waves of rapidly alternating compression and rarification in the air. Radio waves are waves in which electromagnetic effects are propagated through space or, if you prefer to call it by its old name, through the ether.* In waves on the deep sea each particle of water goes round in a vertical circle,

* Ordinary air has a quite negligible effect on the propagation of radio waves, but the upper atmosphere which contains a large number of free electrons can in certain circumstances reflect the waves and so promote their propagation round the earth.

moving forwards on the crest of a wave and backwards on the trough. In sound waves the air moves to and fro along the direction in which the wave is being propagated. In radio waves the electric force, which is what the aerial usually detects, is at right-angles to the direction in which the wave is going, and oscillates backwards and forwards across it. The number of times a second (which is called the frequency) that the complete process repeats at any particular place varies enormously, even with waves for which the distance between successive crests, or whatever is the equivalent extreme state, is the same. If this distance (called the wavelength) is one metre, then the frequency for water waves is 1·25, for sound waves is 340, which corresponds to a note near the middle of the piano, and for radio is 300 million and is in the region used for television. These differences are the direct consequences of the very different speeds of propagation of water waves, sound waves and radio waves. But in spite of these great differences, both in the medium and in speed of propagation and in the character of what is propagated, all waves are instances of *continuous change*, in which what happens at one place is the consequence of what happens at a place a little further back. They all share also another very important property known technically as 'interference'. This means that two waves may at certain places and at certain times cancel one another. If, for example, the trough of one water wave should occur at the same place and time as the crest of another, the two will cancel. This cancellation will, in most cases, not be permanent at any one place, but it is possible to form arrangements of waves for which it is; in such a case there are regions of calm alternated by regions of great disturbance, these last being places where the troughs occur simultaneously and then a moment later the crests, also together. The waves are said to be 'in phase' at these latter places and 'out of phase' where they cancel. Unfortunately water waves are usually too irregular for these effects to be seen clearly, though everyone who has sailed is aware of the existence of temporary patches of relative calm, even in a fairly heavy sea.

Interference can be shown in the case of waves of light, which are similar to those of radio but much shorter, by an experiment which goes back to the beginning of the nineteenth century, and is due to Young. For this experiment light from a very narrow slit illuminates a screen pierced with two other slits very close together, all three slits being parallel. If the light that gets through this screen is then received on another screen it will be found that instead of seeing two bright lines as one would expect from consideration of rays, one sees instead a series of shaded bands parallel to the slits. If the light is white these bands are coloured and only a few can be seen. If the yellow light from a strong sodium lamp is used the bands are black and yellow and can be numerous. The bright bands occur at places where the waves from the two latter slits arrive in phase, and the black bands in between are the places where they arrive just out of phase, so that the effect of one cancels that of the other. If instead of having only two parallel slits one has a great number equally spaced, the bright bands become much sharper and brighter, and the black areas correspondingly larger, thus the bands become bright lines on a black background. Such an arrangement of slits is called a *diffraction grating*.

One generally considers that sound goes round corners while light does not. Actually this is merely a matter of degree. Sound is, in fact, very greatly attenuated by an obstacle, while by careful experiments it was shown as far back as the seventeenth century that light does, in fact, bend slightly into the shadow. The difference is one of degree and corresponds simply to the great difference in the wavelength of the waves concerned. For typical light this is $\frac{1}{50000}$ of an inch, while for sound the waves are in the region of a few feet. The differences are, in fact, completely explained by this consideration. But this implies that all very short waves do, in fact, propagate their effects very nearly in straight lines. They can be described as rays, and motion in a straight line is according to Galileo and Newton the property of a particle on which no force is acting. It was probably this consideration which led Newton to believe that light consists of particles, and as we shall see he was not wholly wrong. In speaking of short waves I mean short in relation to the other lengths concerned, the height of the building, shall we say, in the case of

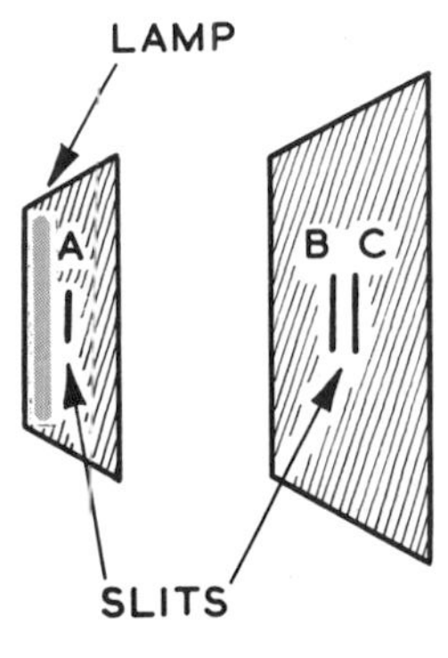

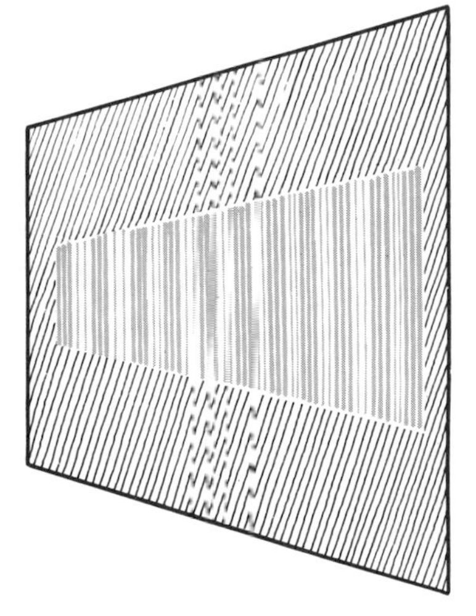

Fig. 16. Young's Interference Experiment

Slit A is needed to get a fine beam of light which then goes through slits B and C, also very fine. The beams AB, AC spread horizontally by diffraction and overlap on the last screen giving the bands as shown (the width and spacing of these are exaggerated for clearness).

sound going from one street to the next, and the object casting the shadow in the case of light.

The particles of Newton, like grains of sand, have nothing about them which recalls the specific properties of waves such as interference. If two particles occur together there are just two particles, and not sometimes 0 and sometimes 4 as would happen if they were waves. But the new idea is that in the case of the very small, this, or something rather like it, in fact happens. That the new particle has some of the properties of a wave. We must explain this in more detail.

Instead of a moving electron having a definite trajectory like a shell shot from a gun, one is only allowed to consider its beginning and its end, by which I mean the places where it has produced, or will produce, some definite effect. In the modern view it is meaningless to ask what it does in between. Now this is not unreasonable, for unless you are prepared to put some kind of a screen up to catch it, like the screens of wires through which bullets are shot to measure their velocity, you cannot say where, in fact, it has gone or when, except only for its start and finish. In the case of a shell from a gun screens can be provided which detect it but hardly disturb it. In the case of the electron this, as we shall see, cannot be done. Anything which detects it will in fact disturb it and must be regarded as, so to speak, its temporary target.

The new theory depends vitally on this matter of observation and of the disturbance which always accompanies observation. It is a 'quantum theory'. The quantum in question is a *unit* of what is called 'action'. This is a mathematically defined quantity in theoretical mechanics which was introduced by the great Irish mathematician William Rowan Hamilton more than a century ago. We do not need to consider it in detail but changes in it correspond very roughly to the extent to which one body influences another or charges itself. If 'action' can only occur in discrete units, then if any influence occurs it cannot be less than one of these units, and if the thing we are interested in affects a detector at all it is bound itself to undergo a certain minimum interference. Strictly speaking this is as true of the shell as of the electron, but while the disturbance in the first case causes a wholly negligible effect because of the great momentum of the shell, it will always be important for an electron and may be overwhelming.

Let us stop again for a moment to consider how an electron can be detected. Fast electrons, like alpha particles, produce scintillations in certain crystals. These are weaker than those caused by the more energetic alphas which Rutherford used, but may be magnified by photoelectric cells and recorded electrically. Another detector is the Geiger counter, a tube usually containing a mixture of argon and an organic gas under an electric tension just too low to give a discharge. The electron will trigger the discharge and the resulting pulse of current can be counted, the device automatically resetting itself ready for the next electron. Both these methods need energetic electrons, and only tell one that the electron has gone through the instrument somewhere in the rather large sensitive region. More accurate positions can be given by the Wilson chamber or by special photographic plates. In the Wilson cloud chamber the path of an ionizing particle such as a fast electron is made visible by the positions of the tiny individual water drops which are formed on the charged particles, the ions, when an artificial cloud is formed by expanding the moist air in the chamber. In the photographic plate the passage of a fast electron can be seen after development as a series of black dots each representing a grain of silver bromide in the photographic emulsion which has been sensitized by the passage of the electron. In these last two cases one can see a *track*, the path of the electron. But at each point where the electron produces a detectable effect, for example a sensitized grain or a pair of ions, it will be deflected in an unknown and unpredictable direction so that its path is not straight but bent in an erratic way.

To detect slow electrons it is usual to accelerate them by an electric force and then detect them in one of the ways mentioned above. If an electron is emitted for example from a zinc plate by the action of ultraviolet light (p. 34), it comes out gently but can then be accelerated by a voltage applied between the plate and a parallel wire grid, rather as a skier may push himself forward over a small hump at the beginning of a run and then gain a high speed by the action of gravity.

The most direct proof of the wave-like nature of electrons, though not the first indication, was given by the behaviour of electrons passing through, or reflected from, metallic crystals.* The atoms in a metallic, or indeed in any, crystal are aligned in parallel rows which extend through the crystal only interrupted by imperfections of growth (Fig. 1). The space between any adjacent two of these parallel rows can be regarded as a slit and the crystal as a large number of parallel slits, in fact a diffraction grating as described above. If the crystal is very thin fast electrons can go through without much other disturbance. The crystal is used because the slits are required to be very close together, and it is difficult (though not with a suitable arrangement impossible) to make such slits artificially. When the experiment is done it is found that the electrons, which are received on a photographic plate, blacken it in a pattern precisely as would be expected for light of a certain wavelength. The pattern is somewhat complicated by the arrangement of atoms in a real crystal not being quite as simple as I have suggested above, especially when the metal film is composed, as it often is, of a number of separate crystals, but the complicated patterns can be accounted for in detail assuming that the electrons behave as waves of a wavelength depending on their speed. The relation between speed, mass, and wavelength includes the quantity h. This is Planck's quantum of action which he introduced in the year 1900 to account for some properties of the thermal radiation from a hot body, and which had in the intervening time played a varied and important role in physics. The experiments were suggested by a theory put forward by L. de Broglie according to which *any* particle should have a wave associated with it according to a stated law.† This law was completely confirmed by the experiments, as far that is as electrons are concerned. It has since been

* This was first shown in 1927 by Davisson and Germer in New York, and shortly after, independently, by the author in Aberdeen. The description in the text refers to the author's method, see Fig. 17.

† The law is: wavelength = h divided by the momentum of the particle.

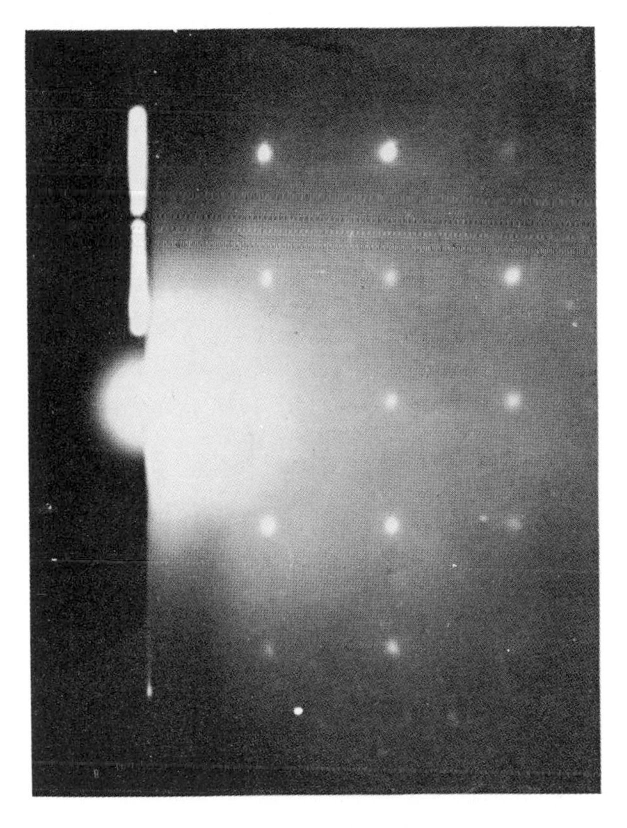

FIG. 17. DIFFRACTION PATTERN

Made by electrons which have been through small roughnesses on a crystal of silver, whose shadow is seen to the left. (Disregard the white vertical line, a fiducial mark made after the main experiment.) The crystal acts like two diffraction gratings crossed with their lines at right-angles. A point source of electrons is used, not a slit as in an ordinary optical spectroscope, so the pattern is one of points not lines. The roughnesses are equivalent to the 'thin film' of the text.

confirmed, though the experiments are more difficult, for protons and helium atoms.

This shows that particles, somehow and sometimes, behave like waves. For twenty years evidence had been accumulating that light sometimes behave like particles. Light had for a century been treated as waves, which explains with great success many beautiful and complicated experiments (Fig. 16), but it also shows a curious behaviour which is called the photoelectric effect. Light falling on a zinc plate, and indeed many other bodies, will eject electrons (p. 34). These electrons come out with an energy which does not depend on the strength of the light, but only on its colour, which corresponds, in the language of the wave theory, to its frequency (p. 111). Making the light stronger gives *more* electrons, not faster ones. This is very unlike the way waves would act, and comes to saying that a gentle swell would throw pebbles up a beach as violently as a great gale though fewer of them. But it is what one would expect from particles. If a building is attacked by rifle bullets the size of the chips knocked off the stone will not depend on how many bullets hit (excluding the rare chance of two hitting the same place at once). Perhaps, however, there is some mechanism in the zinc which can collect energy from the waves till something bursts, and then throw an electron out with an energy determined by the mechanism, like a bolt from a crossbow? But when one came to calculate how long it would take the energy from a weak beam of light to wind up the imaginary crossbow it came out as a substantial time. If X-rays, which are only very extreme ultra-violet light, were used it should take a matter of years, while no delay in the appearance of the electrons could ever be detected, not even a millionth of a second.

This paradox, and others, worried physicists for many years. It seemed that Nature was irrational, a curious feeling that those who experienced it will not forget. De Broglie's theory turned the flank of the paradox by saying that it is no paradox but in the nature of things, and the electron experiments supported him. That these things do not happen in ordinary life is no difficulty; since h is a small quantity one can show that the only cases where they should be noticeable are *either* where a wave has a very great frequency *or* a particle has a very small momentum, which in practice means a very small mass not much more than that of an electron. To regularize matters, the particles which we shall suppose exist in light, are called 'photons'. Since they travel with the speed of light they would have infinite mass and energy if they had any 'rest mass'. Therefore they must have zero rest mass but acquire finite mass, momentum and energy when going with the speed of light. Einstein had in fact suggested twenty years before de Broglie's theory that light went in 'quanta', each of energy $h\nu$ where ν is the frequency of the light. Photons only exist when moving with the speed of light, they cannot be collected in a bottle. Though electrons and photons are both examples of de Broglie's particles and the same general arguments apply to both, it is easier to think about electrons as this avoids having to deal with relativity, since the electrons need not go fast and in what follows we shall limit the argument to them.

Now consider what we have done. Virtually, we have got over the photoelectric paradox and explained the new experiments with electrons at the expense of jettisoning Newton's laws of motion. The movements of particles are somehow to be connected with waves; roughly speaking the particles appear where the waves are strong. But waves, as we have seen, do not go in straight lines; never accurately, at best approximately, even when the waves are short. Hence Galileo's idea of the particle acted on by no force which goes on for ever in a straight line must be abandoned. It is not that the particle would stop but that it would spread, for that is what waves do if they go through a slit or hole as common experience shows with sound. But how can a *particle* 'spread'? It spreads in the sense that you can no longer tell where it will be except that it will be somewhere in the wave. Put rather more formally, the intensity of the wave is a measure of the *probability* of finding the electron at a particular place if a detector is placed there. The waves are a way of calculating where the electron (or the photon) can go, but *not*, and this is an essential point, precisely where it actually does go. The waves are ghosts, they cannot be detected as such, only by the intervention of the electrons as particles which alone blacken the grains in the photographic plate or make the crystal scintillate.

It is not necessary to know (and it is perhaps meaningless to ask) what medium carries the waves or what the physical quantity is which corresponds to the movement of a drop of water, or to the change in pressure of the air in a sound wave. The waves have fulfilled their function when they have said where the electron is likely to be.

De Broglie's original theory was more suggestive than precise,

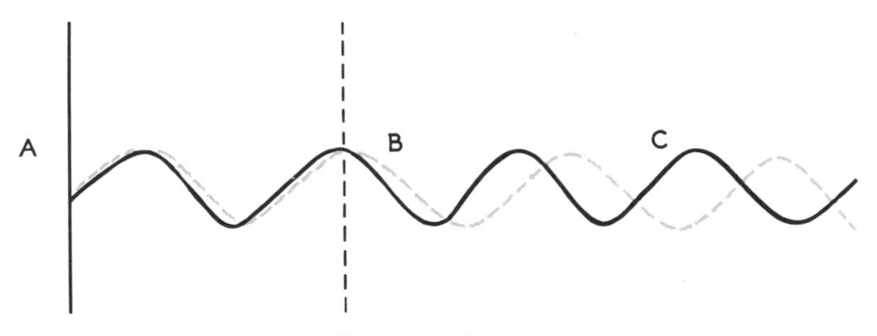

FIG. 18. WAVES IN A LIMITED REGION

The waves are hardly distinguishable to begin with, say in *AB*, but get more and more out of phase and begin to cancel at about *C*.

If one is limited to observations in *AB* either wave fits and the wavelength is to this extent uncertain.

but Schrödinger and others have elaborated it into a mathematical theory known as Wave Mechanics, which is capable of predicting the consequences of almost any possible experiment. One of the curious things about this theory is the parallelism between wave and particle properties. In a sense one can have whichever one wants but not both at the same time. If one designs an experiment which should detect them like that described above, the waves appear. Experiments can be devised which should detect particle properties, such as the conservation of momentum in collisions and they also work, but the circumstances in which the one set of effects can be observed exclude the

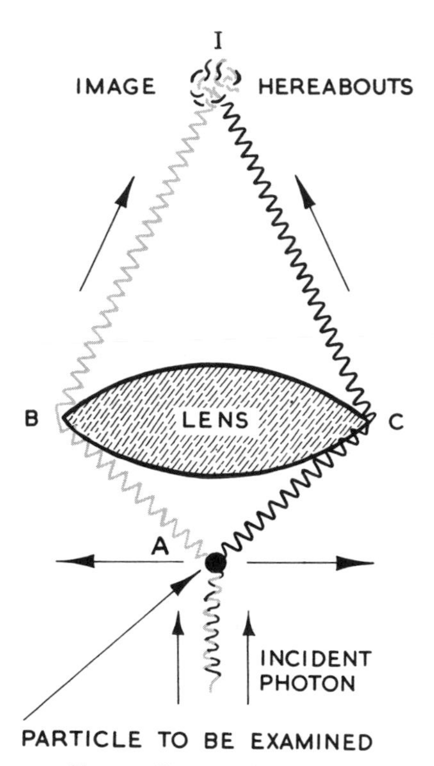

FIG. 19. PHOTON MICROSCOPE

ABI, *ACI*, are possible paths for a photon. *ACI* will kick the electron to left, *ABI* will kick it to the right. Note that by a well-known result in microscopy the angle *BAC* must be large if the image region is to be as small as possible, i.e. about half a wave across.

other, and conversely. Niels Bohr calls this relationship 'complementarity'.

It is illustrated by a principle due to Heisenberg and called the 'uncertainty principle' which says that observations of position and of momentum are mutually exclusive. If one is accurate the other must be inaccurate. Wave mechanics asserts that all the information one can have about an electron is contained in the wave. If then one knows that the wave is limited to a small region of space the electron must be somewhere in this region, but if this region only allows room for a few wavelengths one cannot say just what the wavelength is, quite a range would fit equally well. But wavelength and momentum are inversely proportional, one increases when the other decreases, so if one is uncertain the other must be so as well. If on the other hand you take a long train of waves then the momentum can be well determined, but they will occupy much space and the electron can be anywhere there. This is the wave way of looking at the matter.

The particle way tries to *locate* an electron as a particle by looking at it in a microscope, using some sort of light. This light according to a well-established result in microscopy can only locate the particle to a little better than a wavelength, and the more accuracy one wants the shorter this must be, to be much use the 'light' would have to be X-rays. But the light, or X-rays, has particles also, namely its photons, which have momentum and give an impulse to the electron in some unknown direction when the light shines on it, so its final momentum is uncertain by about the momentum of the photon, which is greater the shorter the wavelength,* even if the light is so faint that there is only one photon this will happen, and it cannot have less and be light at all. One is back with identically the same dilemma, looked at in a different way.

Once one accepts waves as a concommitant of particles and the electron as being both, one is forced to abandon the possibility of accurate prediction on the scale of the very small. This is primarily because the meaning of the waves is simply to state a probability of the electron's presence. If one could concentrate its waves to a mathematical point then one could say that the electron must be there, but however much one focuses waves there is always at best a region of disturbance about half a wavelength in any direction. This is because waves are essentially continuous in sharp contrast to an ideal particle. Even apart from this one could not make precise predictions; because of the Heisenberg principle one

* Because the shorter the wavelength the greater the frequency, to which the energy of the photon is proportional

cannot fix the starting conditions for an electron. Astronomers can predict the motion of a planet with an accuracy that only depends on the skill of their measurements, because the observations do not affect the motion of the planet and its orbit can be determined by a long series of observations, each of which increases the accuracy of prediction. But each observation of an electron disturbs it in an *unpredictable way*, so there is nothing gained by repeating it. Since one cannot know accurately where the electron was to start with, and how fast it was going, there is no hope of predicting where it will be later on. Notice that the Heisenberg principle depends on the fact that light also has particles, the photons, and that these will transmit momentum. If light were 'pure' waves it would only exert a gentle steady pressure on the electron which could be allowed for, and besides one could make the light as weak as one liked and so reduce its disturbing effect. But one cannot detect less than a quantum of light, one photon; it just isn't light at all. So this way out is barred.

Before considering the very important consequences of this conclusion it is desirable to refer briefly to some other divisions of the quantum theory. The relation between frequency and energy $E = h\nu$ is historically the starting point of the whole theory though it can now be treated as a deduction from general wave mechanics. It was used by Planck, in a slightly different form, to explain the spectrum of the light from an ideal black body, and by Einstein to explain the photoelectric effect. This close connection between frequency and energy explains also why light hard solids, in particular diamond, show abnormalities in their heat behaviour at low temperatures. Roughly speaking, the frequency of their atoms is so high, and the quantum of energy therefore so large, that at low temperatures they cannot get enough heat to vibrate and most of the atoms are at rest.

Planck's constant also determines the size of atoms. There is nothing built in to the solar system to determine the absolute size of the orbits of the planets. They might all be twice, or half, as large as they actually are and the system work equally well. The actual sizes must be consequences of the still unknown historical events which created the planets. But atoms have definite sizes;

all carbon atoms for example have the same size, even those of different isotopes. How does this happen? Niels Bohr first gave an answer in terms of *h*. His theory was incomplete and I shall not give it here, though it immensely helped the development of physics for twelve critical years. In terms of waves the answer, crudely, is that the size is such that a wave fits neatly round the atom and finishes where it began. If a room is papered all round with patterned wallpaper there will usually be an awkward join where the pattern does not fit, but if the size of the room is just right for the size of the pattern it will accommodate a whole number of units and fit at the joint. Similarly with waves of an electron going round an atom. In the case of an atom one must remember that the length of the wave will depend on the speed of the electron and this will be increased by the attraction of the positive electric charge on the nucleus. The resulting mathematics is complex even in the simplest case of hydrogen with its one electron, and virtually impossible for really complicated atoms, but certain checks can be made even there, and for hydrogen it works exactly. But there is a peculiar limitation in this theory. One cannot trace the path of the electron as a moving thing. If one tries to determine its position the Heisenberg principle shows that the photon will usually give it such a blow as to knock it out of the atom. Any attempt at tracing the path is impossible. Yet there is some meaning in saying that some, though not all, of the electrons are moving round the nucleus. They give the whole atom a spin, like a top, and alter its behaviour as a whole.

Now let us return to the consequences of indeterminacy, which for a generation has been accepted by the great majority of physicists as a fundamental limitation on knowledge. The novelty is not that experiments are inaccurate, of course they always have been and always will be, but that there is a limit beyond which accuracy cannot be pushed no matter how much care and ingenuity is used. Physics is used to saying what cannot be *done*, e.g. perpetual motion. For the first time it says what cannot be *known*.

Since the time of Newton, at latest, it has been assumed that the inanimate world (at least) is determined that events follow in a predictable sequence. The evidence for this is largely the great success astronomers have had in predicting the motion of the planets. The last discrepancy, the shift in the perihelion of Mercury, has been removed by the general theory of relativity, which really represents the last of the old physics. Wave mechanics of course does not affect the planets, they are so massive that the theoretical limitation on accuracy could never conceivably be reached even in the pipe-dream of the most optimistic astronomers, indeed the same holds even for accurate laboratory apparatus such as time-keeping pendulums. But it is very different at an atomic level.

It is believed with good reason that the ejection of alpha particles from radium and other radioactive substances is an effect of wave mechanics, one which could not occur but for the wave properties of the particles. If for example a Geiger counter has inside it a minute quantity of a substance yielding alphas it will go off whenever one is released. By choosing the amount of the substance one can arrange so that a few counts occur per minute, each shown by an audible click. The average number is definite for a particular amount of material, but the number in any given minute is a matter of chance. If the average is say 12 this is also the most likely number but there will be many minutes when it is 9, 10, 11, 13, 14 or 15, and a few when it differs still more from 12. If wave mechanics is true there is no conceivable way of finding out beforehand what the number will be in any particular minute.

This is just one instance of many varied kinds of observation which are fundamentally uncertain in a way quite independent of defects in the apparatus. They involve individual events, and when there are very many such events the average can be predicted with greater and greater certainty the more there are of them. The experiments with electrons in crystals referred to above come in this category. Very many electrons are needed to produce the patterns. Statistics manufacture certainty out of random events, just as they ensure the profits of Monte Carlo, provided the roulette wheels run truly. It was very repugnant to many scientists to have to think of nature as a kind of glorified roulette wheel, but no generally acceptable alternative has been found in these thirty years and more, and it has not been for want of trying.

Wave mechanics has had many successes in explanation and prediction. There are still many unanswered questions, particularly in the problems of the structure of nuclei, but even here ideas based on wave mechanics have made considerable progress. It seems that we must accept its fundamental principles as, to say the least, much more likely to be true than any other, and in particular than the old Newtonian determinism. This of course makes a very profound difference to the philosophy of science, but looking back one may wonder whether the old determinate belief was really so tenable even in cases when the existence of *h*, on which all the above argument hinges, can be neglected.

Take for example the case of a gas in a container. The kinetic theory of the nineteenth century (which we retain in great part) pictured this as an enormous number of molecules of various shapes, but sometimes for simplicity assumed spherical, rushing about in random directions, colliding with one another and with the walls of the vessels. The collisions are supposed elastic, so no kinetic energy is lost though it is transferred from one molecule to another and back again. In consequence, at any one instant some molecules will be moving fast and others slow, but after another few collisions all memory of the former state of motion is lost. Each molecule makes billions of collisions a second. The hotter the gas the greater is the average speed of the molecules.

How far can determinism be said to apply to a system of molecules like this? Even if one could find a computer capable of working out the billions of collisions of each of billions of billions of molecules (for ordinary air there are about 27 billion billion in a cubic centimetre) how far could one get? To make the question precise, consider an imaginary experiment, suppose one molecule in the gas in a Geiger counter is radioactive and will sooner or later explode to give an alpha ray able to set off a counter. The Geiger counter shall be double, the two halves separated by a wire grid through which the molecules can pass. The experiment is to see which half of the counter goes off. Of course it must be shielded against cosmic rays and other disturbances. We are allowed to fire the particle in near the grid at a known time, and we ignore wave mechanics. To make the prediction we must calculate each collision which the radioactive particle makes in its zigzag motion through the gas till it reaches a wall where we can suppose it to stick. We can arrange so that it is nearly certain to reach one of the walls and stick there before it explodes; this is merely to get over the difficulty that we do not know just *when* it will explode. Determinism requires that we must first measure the position and velocity of all the molecules near the radioactive one to find which it will collide with, then we must compute the first collision and what direction and speed the radioactive one has afterwards. While this is perhaps conceivable we have only begun, the calculation must be repeated for the next collision and so on. Worse still, all the other molecules are making collisions which must be computed to find where they have got to, for any of them may collide with our molecule during its very zigzag path to a wall. But the really hopeless feature is seen when one comes to consider the sort of accuracy one would need. It does not much matter, for this argument, just what law governs the collisions, so to make it definite suppose they are like those between ideally elastic billiard balls. Now it obviously makes all the difference to a collision whether it is end-on or half-ball. The result is quite changed therefore by an error of a half diameter in the assumed position of either of the molecules. Even a much smaller error will alter quite substantially the angle at which the molecule comes off. This change of angle will greatly affect its position at the next collision, for it goes some thousands of diameters between collisions. At each collision the effect of a small mistake in the supposed position or speed of a molecule gets magnified and it is clear that after a few million collisions—and it will need many more than this to get across the tube—it would require virtually infinite accuracy in our knowledge of the initial conditions for our conclusions to have any value as far as individual collisions are concerned.

We should have to fall back on some statistical argument, which by averaging the effect of individual collisions could only tell us the *probability* of the radioactive molecule having got to various parts of the apparatus.

It does not seem that to assert that such a system is determinate has any useful meaning, though I have ignored h and supposed for the sake of argument that each separate collision is as determinate as for full-sized billiard balls. This kind of indeterminacy

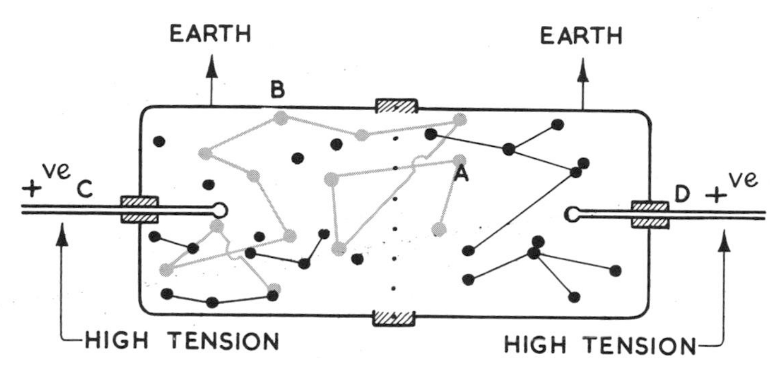

FIG. 20. Imaginary experiment with double Geiger counter and radioactive atom. Path of radioactive atom shown starting from *A*. Gas atoms are in black. There are really some billions of billions of these all colliding with one another millions of times a second and occasionally with the radioactive atom. If the aim is slightly changed in any collision it completely alters the direction of the atom after this collision and so all later collisions. Eventually the radioactive atom drifts to the wall, supposedly at *B*, and sticks there till it explodes and sets off the left-hand Geiger counter by producing a discharge from *C* to the earthed case.

has been pointed out and discussed by Max Born. It does not seem to have been noticed by pre-quantum physicists.

An argument like this shows that indeterminacy may occur even in systems for which the action is a very large multiple of h. To take an example from aerodynamics, the turbulent layer which forms on the surface of streamlined bodies when they move very fast through the air is derived from the lamina flow, which occurs at lower speeds, by the growth of tiny eddies. These are no doubt often determined by small roughnesses in the surface, but if this is very smooth they might quite well come from the very small scale fluctuations in speed and density which are bound to arise from the chance movements of molecules. In a layer which is becoming unstable these small eddies will grow to a great size, but their position and shape at a given time will depend on how they started and so be random. In fact, wherever a system is becoming unstable, which usually happens from it getting too much energy, events on a molecular scale may develop indefinitely in size.

Wave mechanics only come into the argument if someone objects—'but *in principle* one could make the observations to the necessary accuracy and predict it all'. Wave mechanics says that in principle there is a limit to the accuracy and in cases such as those I have sketched the accuracy could never be good enough.

Thus physical events, even some of those on a substantial scale, are sometimes indeterminate to an important extent. The old idea of necessity is restricted to certain classes of events. It may, for example, well be doubted whether long-term meteorological prediction will ever be possible. Whether, for example, one can tell whether there will be open-air skating at Cambridge on New Year's Day, 2060.

It appears obvious to me that if one accepts these kinds of ideas, Nature must seem very different from what it did to a follower of Newton, just as the immense success of Newtonian mechanics as applied to astronomy profoundly affected thought till our time. I find it rather surprising that most professional philosophers, who are of course aware of these ideas, seem inclined to minimize their importance. This is perhaps because the quantum theory has been used rather wildly as an argument for free will. It may or may not be a valid one. If the problem of free will is capable of scientific treatment at all, which seems to me an open question, it is not a matter on which physics can decide. But determinism *is*, and on this matter physicists are agreed with surprisingly few exceptions. We may be wrong, and to err on a matter on which Newton erred would seem almost an honour; but it seems reasonably certain that the error, if it exists, can only be found out by progress in physics; by finding out still more about the way in which different kinds of matter actually behave under what are to us abnormal conditions.

In speaking here of determinism I mean the power of predicting with reasonable accuracy events which will, or will not, be actually observed. The ideal world of mathematics chosen to represent the quantum differs substantially but not fundamentally from that invented by Newton, both predict what will be observed by precisely calculating the values to be assigned to mathematical quantities. The difference lies in the significance of these values. In a typical Newtonian case they stated where something would be at some particular future time; in a typical quantum case they tell you the relative probabilities of certain possible events occurring at or near that time.

The maps of Newtonian and quantum physics (to return to our earlier simile), are both printed on paper and though they differ seem much alike to a cursory glance. The vital difference comes when you come to apply them. The first refers to a world of hard rock where everything is fixed and definite. The second to a world of clouds and oceans agitated into spray by ceaseless gusts, just as real a world as the first but without its sharp edge. Only if one is on a large ship can one ignore the motion.

Even if Nature really knows her own mind, there are certain things she has no intention of letting us know in advance.

MAX PLANCK

It is one of those neat coincidences that history sometimes arranges that the turn of the twentieth century should see the date, within a month, at which was published the most important new idea of the century. In December 1900 Planck put forward the first form of the quantum theory, including the famous Planck's constant *h*. He was not a young man at the time for he was born in the year 1855 at Kiel, where his father was Professor of Law. Like most physicists of his generation he was trained as a mathematician. Unlike many he remained so all his life and did no experimental work, unless one counts a study of a big harmonium built to illustrate the difference between pure and tempered tuning. His early work was on thermodynamics, a branch of physics which in spite of important applications to industrial chemistry and to heat engines can be very abstract. This suited Planck's serious and philosophical outlook, and his discoveries were important enough to win him the Chair of Theoretical Physics at Berlin. In the Reichsanstalt at Berlin, the German National Physical Laboratory, a good deal of work was going on at this time on the radiation produced by hot bodies. This might not seem a very fundamental quantity; it depends in general on the nature of the body, but if one examines the radiation *inside* a hot body it had been proved thermodynamically by Planck's predecessor Kirchoff, and verified experimentally, that it is quite independent of the chemical nature or physical state of the body. If one looks inside a glowing coal fire through a gap between the coals one notices that the edges of the glowing coals are very indistinct. In a more refined experiment in which the viewing post is reduced to a small hole the radiation coming from any portion of the wall is indistinguishable. The radiation that escapes from the hole is known as 'full radiation' or sometimes 'black body' radiation. Because it does not depend on the substance or substances used but only on the temperature, it is clearly something pretty fundamental. As the cavity gets hotter the radiation increases in amount and changes in quality from a dull red containing mostly invisible radiations to a dazzling white which when broken up by a prism shows, like sunlight, all colours including violet. How does the intensity of light of a particular colour vary with the colour, i.e. the wavelength of the light, and with the temperature of the cavity? Before Planck, two formulae had been proposed, one by Wien and one by Rayleigh, each with some theoretical basis. The first worked fairly well for the long wave or red light, the second for the blue and ultraviolet. Planck's first step was to invent a mathematical formula to combine the two. He found one which fitted the experiments for all colours. This formula had at first little theoretical basis though suggested by some earlier mathematics, but Planck soon gave it one. He showed that his formula could be derived in terms of the existing laws of electricity (by then Maxwell's electromagnetic theory of light was fully accepted) but only if it is supposed that light is emitted and absorbed, not continuously as they would naturally lead one to suppose, but in discrete lumps of energy, in 'quanta'. The magnitude of the quantum had to be assumed proportional to the frequency of the light, more for blue than for red. He gave the constant in this proportion sum the symbol h.

It took a good many years for the extreme importance of Planck's discovery to be realized, which is nothing less than the substitution of discontinuity for continuity in a fundamental law of physics. People were interested in the new formula, which certainly fitted the facts, but rather played down the way in which it had been derived. Most people thought that some way would be found of getting what was probably the right formula without making such drastic and revolutionary assumptions. Planck had said nothing about the state of the radiation in space. It was not necessary to assume that it was other than continuous as Maxwell had supposed. Einstein, who was also at Berlin and a great personal friend of Planck's, went a step further in 1905 and supposed that radiation even in space goes in quanta, and $E = h\nu$ became for the first time a familiar sight on the blackboards of physical laboratories. This step greatly helped the spread of the theory especially among the laboratory physicists. It removed it from the rare and abstract air of theoretical thermodynamics which left some of them gasping if respectful, and also explained some very odd facts about X-rays and ultraviolet light which were beginning to be a serious trouble (p. 117). Then in 1913 Niels Bohr put forward his theory of the hydrogen atom in which Planck's conception was applied for the first time to the great problem of atomic structure. After that the development came as we have sketched it in the last chapter, but Planck took little further part.

Planck was essentially a theoretician and all his life was deeply interested in the philosophical aspect of physics. He believed almost passionately in the reality of the external world, and opposed the then fashionable positivist view of Mach and Ostwald, which by limiting physics too strictly to what is immediately observable deadens imagination. Yet he was not a model-maker like J. J. Thomson or Rutherford. He adopted a cautious attitude to the philosophical consequences of his own work and remained a firm believer in causality though he put a rather special interpretation on the term. He rejoiced in pure reason and begins his autobiography with the words:

'My original decision to devote myself to science was a direct result of the discovery which has never ceased to fill me with enthusiasm since my early youth—the comprehension of the far from obvious fact that the laws of human reasoning coincide with the laws governing the sequences of the impressions we receive from the world about us; that, therefore, pure reasoning can enable man to gain an insight into the mechanism of the latter. In this connection, it is of paramount importance that the outside world is something independent from man, something absolute, and the quest for the laws which apply to this absolute appeared to me as the most sublime scientific pursuit in life.'

In his early years recognition of the validity of his thermodynamical ideas was slow in coming, and he seems to have felt this. He was a German of the best kind, upright, scrupulous, dignified; apparently rather stiff yet capable under suitable conditions of unbending surprisingly and with charm. Completely Aryan and strongly patriotic he opposed the treatment of the Jews and at an official visit to Hitler asked for better treatment for certain of them. Hitler became furious and Planck had to leave.

He had ill-fortune in his family; lost a son in the first war and two daughters in childbirth. His last son was executed, with so many of the flower of Germany, in consequence of the July plot against Hitler.

On one occasion at least he expressed in public his firmly held belief in a beneficent deity. It happened that Planck and Einstein were given an honorary degree at the same time at Cambridge. It would be hard to imagine two men less alike in appearance than were Planck and Einstein, the latter so startling, with his shock of grey hair surrounding his bronzed face like a halo, that he could only be taken for a genius or a fanatic.

Planck, on the other hand, looked perfectly normal, except for a certain air of nobility. He had a quiet dignity and gave the impression of being a man of fine and strong character. He was again in Cambridge in 1931, and on both these visits he and his wife stayed with J. J. Thomson at Trinity Lodge. J.J. greatly admired Planck's work, which was rather more in tune with his own line of thought than was that of Einstein, and he enjoyed his company. Planck—fortunately for J.J.—spoke good English, as did his second wife, a sensible kindly woman, devoted to her distinguished husband's welfare.

In some respects Planck and J.J. were not unlike in personality. Both were quite unselfconscious and unassuming, showing a kindly attitude towards people in general and lively interest in matters apart from science.

Both, although much of their work dealt with abstractions, were very realistic in their outlook towards everyday events. Apart from science, Planck had two absorbing interests, music and mountain climbing. Einstein was likewise a musician and while he lived in Germany he and Planck frequently played together—Einstein on the violin and Planck on the piano.

Planck continued to be an active mountaineer well into his old age, and his deep love for mountains and the open country was a strong feature of his personality.

An example both of his vigour in old age and of his courtesy was his accompanying J.J.'s daughter, who was passing through Berlin late at night, to her train when he was nearly eighty, though he was starting early next morning for a day in the country.

It is very fitting that the Max Planck Gesselschaft which is the leading organization for science in the post-war Reich should have been named after this great physicist and noble character.

C. J. DAVISSON

DAVISSON's career is interesting even apart from the merit of his discoveries, as being one of the first examples of work of the highest importance in pure science carried out in an industrial laboratory. In fact Davisson was a man of thirty-six with a very high reputation in the physics of ions and electrons when in 1917 he went for what was supposed to be a short war-time appointment with what is now the Bell Telephone Laboratories and was then part of Western Electric Company's organization. He stayed there till 1946 when he retired to live in Charlottesville, where he held a post as research professor at the University of Virginia till his death in 1958.

His most important work was to provide the first direct experimental evidence that electrons can behave like waves. The particular way in which he did so was to copy what happens when light is reflected from a solid surface closely ruled with parallel lines or transmitted through a glass plate ruled in the same way. Both act fundamentally alike, the light is broken up by such a 'grating' into its component colours as though it had been through a prism. For electrons 'colour' is replaced by speed, and in Davisson's case the 'grating' was a complex one consisting of the criss-cross lines of atoms on the exposed surface of a crystal of nickel. The ruled surface is called in optics a 'diffraction grating' and the experiments of Davisson are spoken of as 'electron diffraction'.

To a student of scientific method it is interesting that Davisson's discovery was not initially the consequence of a desire to test a theory. In this, his experiments differed from mine, which were inspired by the ideas of Prince L. de Broglie. Davisson was interested in the behaviour of scattered electrons before de Broglie's theory had appeared; these led to surprising results and the theory was called in to explain them.

On the return of peace Davisson began to work on the more fundamental physics of the thermionic valves he had studied in war-time. He was allowed a great measure of freedom in choosing his research, a tribute to his obvious outstanding ability. One thing led to another and by 1921 he was working on the so-called 'secondary electrons' that appear when electrons hit a solid surface. A good deal of not very satisfactory work had been done on this subject, which is difficult because the effects depend greatly on the state of the surface, on whether it is really clean (which it very seldom is, for it is very difficult to remove layers of gas which cling to the surface even in a good vacuum) or, if dirty, of what the dirt consists. Davisson, with Kunsman to help him, working on nickel under unusually good vacuum conditions, found that many of the secondary electrons came off the surface in a few well marked directions which they called peaks. They tried explanations of these peaks which were not very convincing. In 1925, after studying some other metals, Davisson returned to nickel. Up till now the experiments had all been on ordinary nickel which is composed of a large number of very small crystals, but by an accident to the liquid air-trap the specimen became oxidized, and in restoring the surface by heating it was changed into an aggregate of only a few large crystals. There was a complete alteration in the pattern of scattering, though the peaks were even more prominent. The old theories had to be abandoned and a new one was suggested based on an idea of 'transparent directions' in the crystal. However, this did not last either; partly as a result of a visit to the British Association meeting in Oxford, Davisson came to believe that his result was connected with the new theory of de Broglie. By improving his technique and working with a target in which one crystal occupied the whole surface he and his co-worker Germer got results in January 1927 which made sense according to the theory. It is quite a complicated matter, for though the effect of the surface layer of atoms predominates, the next three or four layers make an appreciable difference, which it was not then possible to calculate precisely. In consequence some of the results were a little difficult to interpret, but the great majority were in striking agreement with de Broglie's theory, and were accepted as proving it.

This was indeed a triumph of experimental skill. The relatively slow electrons Davisson and Germer used (about 150 volts energy) are most difficult to handle. If the results are to be of any value the vacuum has to be quite outstandingly good. Even now, when immense advances have been made in vacuum technique it would be a very difficult experiment. In those days it was a veritable triumph. It is a tribute to Davisson's experimental skill that only two or three other workers have used slow electrons successfully for this purpose, though Germer has recently introduced an improvement in technique which may make it much easier. In contrast, the method I used with fast electrons (30,000 volts or more) has had many applications because it is relatively easy to use.

Davisson had some of the conventional qualities of the scientist, such as shyness, but he was very far indeed from being a type. He was a man of exceptional attraction. I have never met anyone who did not like Davisson, such people do not exist. Yet he was not immediately impressive. He was slight in build and with a hesitant manner of speaking which made him seem shyer than he really was. In spite of this he had the reputation of being readily accessible in the laboratory and most helpful to the many who consulted him. Though he worked so long in industrial laboratories he was essentially an individualist, working with at most one or two other people and doing much with his own hands. His influence however extended far, and a number of the leading names in present-day American physics came under it. He had a delightful sense of humour and was full of quiet fun, sometimes unexpected.

X

SOME CONCLUSIONS

I HOPE I have made it clear that research, in physics at least, is very much a hit or miss affair. The great strength of science is that the hit rings a loud bell, or, to change the metaphor, that a success unlocks a door through which one can pass to an unsuspected room. A discovery, whether experimental or theoretical, suggests new experiments, often new techniques. These are applied in other branches of science and in industry so that after a few years what was a troublesome and delicate effect only made to work after much expert labour and at that still precarious, becomes embodied in a device used by housewives. I am lost in admiration at the skill shown by engineers in making physical experiments reliable. The domestic television set is a miracle, not so much that something of the kind could be made to work for a few minutes after weeks of work by the people who had designed it but that it runs so reliably with the minimum of maintenance. Here is the uniformity of nature at last!

This connection between scientific discovery and ordinary life is to my mind very important, not only for the man in the street but for the scientist. Whatever one may think of the social influence of television no one can doubt that it works, and what is true of television is true of a dozen other things. No earlier philosophy has ever had this close connection with everyday life, which makes it part of common sense. Whatever views you have about the world they have got to be consistent with television, and the rest, all working. This means that in some sense our ideas are right. This does not prove them unique. It may be possible to say the same thing, or very nearly the same thing, in several apparently widely different ways. There are examples of this in physics. But the present set of ideas is one valid over a very wide range. It is fairly simple and even if the concepts on which it is based are shown to correspond to reality only over a limited range, they will probably be retained over that range, following the precedent of the light-ray. The present theory of the electron is certainly incomplete; there are things it does not predict. One cannot tell what form the necessary modification may take. It may or may not be fundamental. But even if it is as fundamental a change as that between Newtonian time and the time of relativity, I expect that it will not alter the practice (or the textbooks) of electronics much more than Einstein has altered the design of clocks.

The pyramid of physical science rests securely on the wide base of the successful explanation of large areas of fact in terms of concepts; some of these concepts are themselves explained as examples, usually only approximately valid, of others more fundamental. These last are still open to question and modification and it is this that gives physics its special excitement and interest.

Perhaps they will some day all be seen as examples of some all-embracing principle, but I doubt it. What my father wrote some thirty years ago is still true:

'A great discovery is not a terminus, but an avenue leading to regions hitherto unknown. We climb to the top of the peak and find that it reveals to us another higher than any we have yet seen, and so it goes on. The additions to our knowledge of physics made in a generation do not get smaller or less fundamental or less revolutionary, as one generation succeeds another. The sum of our knowledge is not like what mathematicians call a convergent series . . . where the study of a few terms may give the general properties of the whole. Physics corresponds rather to the other type of series called divergent, where the terms which are added one after another do not get smaller and smaller, and where the conclusions we draw from the few terms we know, cannot be trusted to be those we should draw if further knowledge were at our disposal.'

GLOSSARY

Active deposit. When a radioactive gas such as radium is near a solid surface some of the atoms resulting from the radioactivity reach the surface and stick there. These daughter atoms are themselves often radioactive and constitute an 'active deposit'.

Alpha rays. The least penetrating of the three kinds of radiation, alpha, beta and gamma, produced by naturally radioactive substances. Though penetrating only a few centimetres of air at ordinary density they are hard to deflect by electric or magnetic fields. They are identical with the nuclei of atoms of helium moving at high speed.

Atom. The smallest part of an element which has the distinctive chemical properties of the element. About 100 million atoms would take up an inch.

Atomic number. When the elements are arranged in order of increasing atomic weight (modified in a few cases) its position in this order is called the atomic number of the element. Thus the first element hydrogen has atomic number 1 and the last of them naturally occurring, which is uranium, has number 92. Moseley showed that atomic number is equal to the electric charge on the nucleus in electronic units.

Atomic weight. The weight of an atom in units which make that of the commonest isotope of carbon exactly 12 (till last year the standard was oxygen taken as 16, the difference is very slight). The chemical atomic weight of an element is the average weight of the isotopes in the normal natural mixture.

Baryons. A group of sub-atomic particles of which the lightest are protons and neutrons, the rest being unstable particles produced in the atmosphere by very energetic cosmic rays.

Beta rays. Fast electrons emitted by some radioactive atoms, natural or artificial, when their nuclei are transformed.

Cathode. *See* Electrode.

Cathode rays. Electrons emitted from the negative pole or cathode when an electric discharge passes through a gas at a suitable density, usually a thousandth of that of atmospheric air or less.

Condenser (electrical). Now often called a 'capacitator'; a device for storing a considerable electric charge at a moderate potential (voltage). Often made of thin sheets of metal interleaved by others of an insulating material.

Condenser (steam). A vessel where steam from the exhaust of an engine is cooled and turned to water.

Crystal. A solid in which the atoms are arranged in groups which repeat regularly throughout the crystal like the pattern of a wallpaper.

Diffraction grating. A device for separating light into its component colours, thus acting like a prism. In its simplest form it is a glass plate ruled on one side in parallel lines very evenly and accurately spaced; about 10,000 lines to the inch is usual.

Efficiency of engine. For a mechanical device such as a screw-jack, the efficiency is the useful work delivered divided by the work put in. For a heat engine it is the useful work delivered divided by the work equivalent to the heat put in.

Electric charge. Objects are said to be electrically charged when they exert forces on one another which can be described by the laws of electricity, one of which is that when the objects are small the forces vary inversely as the square of the distance between them. Charges are of two kinds; like charges repel and unlike attract. One is called positive, the other negative. Equal positive and negative charges cancel but it is an arbitrary convention (due to Benjamin Franklin) which is called positive. Electrons are negative and protons positive. Equal numbers of electrons and protons produce normal neutral matter.

Electrolysis. When an electric current passes through a non-metallic liquid chemical, decomposition occurs, and the products are released at the electrodes. (*See* below).

Electrode, cathode, anode. Electrodes are the metal conductors by which an electric current is conveyed in or out of a liquid or gas. The cathode is the negative electrode, the anode the positive one, a conventionally positive current flows from anode to cathode in the liquid or gas. Since electrons are negative any part of the current carried by them will be due to electrons moving from cathode to anode.

Electron. Electrons are the lightest entities known to possess mass when at rest. They show the characteristic mixed behaviour of quantum 'particles', sometimes behaving like small bodies of ordinary experience, at other times like waves. Ordinary electrons have negative charges. Positive electrons, however, can exist for a short time.

Ellipse 8. A curve such that the sum of the distances of any point on it from two fixed points, called the foci, is constant. Can be drawn with the help of a string tied to two pins representing the foci.

Emanation. Gas emitted from certain radioactive substances, of which radium is one. Emanations are themselves radioactive, and deposit radioactive contamination on surfaces which they reach.

Energy. One of the most fundamental quantities of physics. It can take many forms, kinetic, gravitational, heat, electromagnetic, etc., and be transferred from one body to another, but the total amount in any isolated region is constant. Einstein showed that mass is itself a form of energy. Nuclear energy comes from the masses of the nuclei concerned.

Ether. An all-pervading medium formerly supposed to transmit the waves of light.

Force. That which changes or tends to change the state of rest or uniform motion of a body.

Frame of reference. A set of lines or planes (often imaginary) with respect to which the positions of objects can be measured. For example: lines of latitude and longitude, or the floor of a room and two walls meeting in a corner.

Field (electric, magnetic, gravitational). A region of space in which the effect in question is detectable. At each point of this region there is a direction in which the effect is exerted, e.g. vertically downwards for the gravitational field of the earth.

Frequency. When a motion or other event recurs at regular intervals the number of times it happens per second is called the frequency.

Gamma rays. The most penetrating of the rays from radioactive substance. They are identical in nature with X-rays, but are mostly produced in the nuclei of atoms.

Gravitation. On Newton's theory, is the force of mutual attraction between all bodies of the universe taken in pairs. Also used for any other theory which accounts for the kind of effects dealt with by Newton's theory.

Helium. A light gas present in certain minerals. It is chemically inert.

Hyperbola. A curve described by certain comets which go round the sun and never return.

Induction coil. A device, now almost obsolete, for making high voltage alternating current from a low voltage direct supply.

Inertia. Another name for mass.

Inertial frame. A frame of reference in which Newton's laws of motion are obeyed (but strictly speaking only for large objects and moderate speeds).

Interference fringes. Alternate light and dark bands of light, which may be straight or curved, produced when two beams of light, originally coming from the same source, are superposed.

Ion. A charged particle which by its motion carries a current. Ions are often of atomic dimensions.

Isotope. A subspecies of atom. The atoms of any one element all have the same charge on the nucleus, but their weight may vary by multiples of a unit. All of the same weight are said to belong to the same isotope.

Kinetic energy. Energy due to motion.

Kinetic theory. A theory which considers the behaviour of matter, and especially of gases, to be due to the motion of the atoms or molecules.

In the case of gases this motion is a random one, constantly interrupted by collisions between the molecules.

Leptons. A class of particles recently discussed which includes electrons as its best-known members. Others are neutrinos and μ mesons. All are much lighter than protons or any of the baryon class.

Magnetic pole. The region of a magnet where the attraction appears concentrated. A more precise definition is possible in mathematical terms, but it is doubtful if the concept is really fundamental.

Mass. The quality which makes it difficult to start a body moving and to stop it once it is in motion.

Mesons. Unstable particles discovered in cosmic rays, they are intermediate in mass between electrons and protons. They can now be made in atomic accelerators, such as those at Brookhaven, U.S.A., and the international CERN laboratory near Geneva.

Molecule. A group of atoms held together by chemical forces.

Momentum. The momentum of a body is the product of its mass and its velocity.

Neutrino. A particle of zero rest mass and no electric charge emitted with beta particles and in some other nuclear transformations. At first it was postulated for theoretical reasons, recently effects due to neutrinos have been detected near a nuclear reactor.

Neutron. A neutral particle of mass slightly greater than a proton, believed to exist stably in most nuclei. Free neutrons, which are the working material in nuclear reactors turn each into a proton and an electron in about fifteen minutes.

Non-Euclidian space. Space in which the Theorem of Pythagoras is not true.

Nucleus. The small but massive inner core of an atom, discovered by Rutherford. It carries a positive electric charge.

Organic chemistry. The chemistry of compounds containing carbon and often but not always associated with living matter.

Particle. A small object. Very small particles have been shown to behave in a way quite contrary to everyday experience.

Photoelectric effect. When ultra-violet light, including X-rays, falls on certain substances electrons are instantaneously emitted.

Photons. Light sometimes behaves as if it were a stream of discrete particles. These are called photons. Like electrons, photons are particles in the quantum sense, i.e. they combine the properties of commonsense particles with those of waves.

Principle of relativity:

Special: Asserts that fundamental laws must have a mathematical form identical for all frames of reference moving with respect to each other with constant linear velocity.

General: Asserts that fundamental laws must have a mathematical form identical for all frames of reference whatever.

Positive rays. Rays sometimes seen proceeding *towards* the cathode when electricity passes through a gas at very low density. To observe them a hole is made in the cathode or better a tube is put through it, the rays being observed as they come out of the tube. Most of them are atoms or molecules which have lost one or more electrons and so are positively charged.

Prout's hypothesis. Prout supposed that all atoms were made of hydrogen and that their weights were exact multiples of the weight of a hydrogen atom.

Protein. A class of complicated organic substances containing long chains of carbon and nitrogen atoms. Proteins are known containing 10,000 atoms in the molecule.

Proton. One of the most fundamental particles of physics. Easily obtained by ionizing hydrogen atoms, i.e. removing the one electron each contains, the residue being a proton. Other nuclei are considered to be built up of protons and neutrons. The proton has a positive electric charge.

Quantum theory. The theory that exchanges of energy take place by discrete steps or quanta proportional to the frequency associated with the process. It has taken several forms of which the accepted one is wave mechanics.

Radiation. Strictly speaking any effect propagated from a source roughly in straight lines. It thus includes alpha rays, cathode rays and others. Sometimes the name is restricted to those radiations which resemble light in being electromagnetic and travelling with a fixed speed, the speed of light. Such radiations include infra red, ultra violet, X-rays and gamma rays.

Radioactivity. A property of certain unstable nuclei, some of which occur in nature, others only when made artificially. A radioactive nucleus disintegrates spontaneously, emitting an alpha or beta ray often accompanied by gamma rays.

Ray of light. A narrow beam of light which can be treated approximately as a mathematical line.

Relativity: *see* Principle of

Rest mass. The mass of an object at rest or moving slowly. When an object moves with a speed comparable with that of light its mass becomes greater than its rest mass.

Semi-conductors. Solids which conduct electricity appreciably but much less than do metals. In many cases this conductivity depends greatly on small amounts of impurity. Germanium and silicon are commercially important semi-conductors. (*See* Transistors.)

Sidereal time. Time as measured by the apparent motion of the stars. There is one more sidereal than solar day in a year.

Spin. A technical term in wave mechanics. Though the spin of an electron, for example, produces some effects which resemble those of a spinning top the analogy must not be pressed too far. In its present use spin can only be defined in mathematical language.

Supernova. The very bright new stars seen about once every two or three hundred years are called supernovae. They are thought to be due to the violent explosion of a star at a certain stage of evolution.

Temperature. The degree of heat of a body.

Tensor calculus. The system of mathematics used in the general theory of relativity.

Theorem of Pythagoras. In a right-angled triangle the square on the hypotenuse is equal to the sum of the squares on the other two sides.

Thermodynamics. The mathematical theory of the exchange between heat and other forms of energy.

Transistors. Devices using semi-conductors to amplify the effects of electric impulses.

Wavelength. The distance in which a wave motion repeats. In a water wave this is the distance from crest to crest or from trough to trough.

Waves. Effects, usually but not necessarily of motion, propagated continuously from point to point.

Wilson cloud-chamber. A device, due to C. T. R. Wilson, for showing the path of a fast particle moving through air, by condensing moisture on the charged atoms or molecules produced in the air of the chamber by the fast particle.

Work. In physics and engineering this word is used in a special sense, namely as the product of a force and the distance its point of application is advanced. In this sense a man does work in lifting a weight, but not in holding it up or carrying it along a level road.

X-rays. Electromagnetic radiation, like ordinary light except that the wavelength is about a thousand times shorter.

INDEX

Subjects dealt with in the Glossary are marked with an asterisk.